PHYSICS HOMEWORK

for OCR A

FOR DOUBLE AND SEPARATE AWARDS

Viv Newman and Vernon Smith

Series editor: Bob McDuell

Heinemann Educational Publishers,
Halley Court, Jordan Hill, Oxford, OX2 8EJ
A division of Reed Educational & Professional Publishing Ltd
Heinemann is a registered trademark of Reed Educational & Professional Publishing Limited

OXFORD MELBOURNE AUCKLAND
JOHANNESBURG BLANTYRE GABORONE
IBADAN PORTSMOUTH NH (USA) CHICAGO

First published 2001

ISBN 0 435 58281 X

05 04 03 02
10 9 8 7 6 5 4 3

Edited by Tim Jackson

Indexed by Indexing Specialists

Typeset and illustrated by 🐦 Tek-Art, Croydon, Surrey

Printed and bound in Great Britain by Scotprint, East Lothian

Acknowledgements
P43 Q9 F Graham Smith *Radio Astronomy* Pelican Publishers 1962.

The publishers have made every effort to trace the copyright holders, but if they have inadvertently overlooked any, they will be pleased to make the necessary arrangements at the first opportunity.

Introduction

This book provides homework for students taking Physics as part of OCR A double-award science or OCR A separate-award physics. It accompanies the student course books for OCR A double-award and separate-award physics (ISBNs 0 435 58295 X and 0 435 58294 1 respectively).

There is one page of homework for each double-page spread in the student course book. This makes it easy to see which homework may be set following lessons based on a particular double-page spread.

Where students can take the course book home, this homework book will supply extra work to be done at home. Where the course book is not available, the homework book provides:

- a list of key points for each spread
- the full and detailed glossary from the separate-award physics course book.

The answers to the questions in the homework book are available on the CD-ROM. They can be used to mark the work or can be printed out and given to students to mark their own work.

The questions in the homework book can be used in lessons where the teacher is absent. Students can work through the relevant double-page spread in the course book and then attempt questions from the homework book. They could then be given the answers from the CD-ROM towards the end of the lesson.

The homework book allows differentiated homework to be set if required. The questions in the homework book are set at two levels:

- ■ standard demand – aimed at C and D grades
- ◆ standard/high demand – aimed at A and B grades.
- ◇ high demand – aimed at A* grade.

Material marked with an **H** is for higher-tier only.

IDEAS AND EVIDENCE questions focus on how science is evaluated and presented, and the power and limitations of science in addressing industrial, social and environmental issues.

For students needing further help there is additional material on the CD-ROM which can be modified to suit the individual needs of students. This could be put together as a booklet for each Teaching block, perhaps incorporating Key Stage 3 Summary sheets and modified Student checklists where statements in bold (H only) are removed.

We hope that this Homework book will help students to be successful.

Contents

Teaching block A1

Electronics and control

Teaching block A2

Processing waves

Teaching block A3

More about forces and energy

1.1 Circuit components

Key points

- Energy is transferred from cells and other sources to make things happen in a complete electrical circuit. Circuit components dissipate this energy, producing heat, light, sound or movement.

- Resistors become hot when charge flows through them.
- Variable resistors alter the current in a circuit.

1 The drawing below shows an electric circuit.

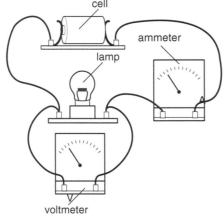

Draw a circuit diagram, using standard symbols, that correctly represents the circuit drawn above.

2 State how energy is mainly dissipated when a power supply is connected to each of the following components:

a lamp   b bell   c motor
d resistor   e LED.

3 The diagram below shows an LED as part of a circuit.

a If this circuit were switched on the LED would be damaged. Why?

b Redraw the circuit and include a device which will protect the LED from damage.

4 The diagram shows a simple light meter.

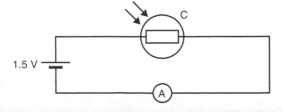

a Name the component labelled 'C'.

b What happens to the resistance of this component when the light shining on it becomes brighter?

The light meter is used to help a cricket umpire to decide whether it is too dark to play safely. The current that flows indicates the brightness as shown on the graph below.

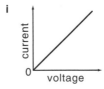

c Copy the graph and, in suitable positions on the brightness axis, write these labels:

- twilight
- bright sunshine
- hazy sunshine
- cloudy.

d Two main areas are marked on the graph. Label one 'too dark to play', and the other 'bright enough to play'.

5 The graphs below show the variation of resistance with temperature for two different electrical components.

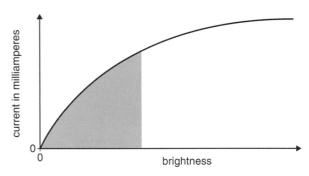

a Write a brief description of the way that resistance varies with temperature for each graph.

b Suggest what component might have been used to obtain the results shown on each graph.

1.2 Measuring resistance

Key points

- An electric current is a flow of charge. It is measured using an ammeter placed in series in a circuit.
- Voltage is a measure of the energy transferred in a component. It is measured using a voltmeter placed in parallel.

- Resistance can be found by finding the current through a resistor and the voltage across it.
- Voltage divided by current gives the resistance value.

---

1 Copy and complete the table below.

voltage in V	current in A	resistance in Ω
6.0	0.20	
	0.54	11.5
9.0		6.0

---

2 The diagram below shows a circuit with some current values marked on.

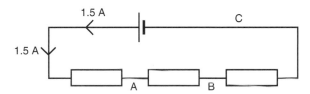

What are the current values at points A, B and C?

---

3 The diagram below shows a circuit with some current values marked on.

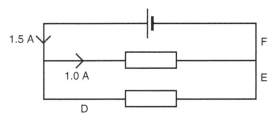

What are the current values at points D, E and F?

---

4 The diagram below shows a circuit with some voltage values marked on.

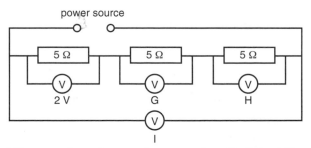

What are the voltage values at points G, H and I?

---

5 The diagram below shows a circuit with some voltage values marked on.

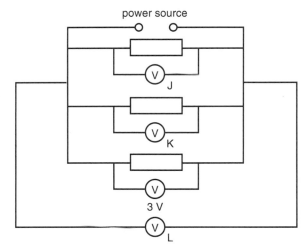

What are the voltage values at points J, K and L?

---

6 The diagram below shows a circuit connected to light some lamps.

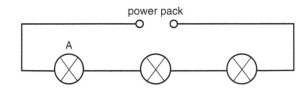

a Copy the diagram, adding an ammeter to measure the current supplied by the power pack and a voltmeter to measure the voltage across lamp A.

b One of the meters has a very high resistance and the other has a very low resistance. Which is which?

c Explain the importance of the high or low resistance of each meter.

1.3 More about resistance

Key points

- Current varies with voltage differently for wires, lamps and diodes.

- The resistance of a light dependent resistor varies with light intensity, and that of a thermistor with temperature.

1

a You have been asked to set up a circuit to measure the current through a resistor and the voltage across the resistor. You have the following apparatus:

- power pack
- switch
- leads
- resistor
- ammeter
- voltmeter.

Draw a circuit diagram to show how you would connect the components.

b Draw another circuit diagram, using the same components, but this time also include a variable resistor so that the current can be changed.

---

2 Using the circuit from question **1**, part **b**, a student obtained these results:

current in A	voltage in V
0	0
0.17	2.0
0.35	4.0
5.10	6.0
0.67	8.0
0.86	10.0

a One of the readings has been taken wrongly. Which do you think it is? What do you think the correct reading should be?

b Plot the graph of current against voltage, using your corrected reading. Draw the best fit straight line.

c Using the values $I = 0.17$ A and $V = 2.0$ V from the table, calculate the resistance of the resistor.

d The student set the power pack to a higher voltage and obtained these readings: $I = 1.60$ A,

$V = 24.0$ V. Calculate the resistance of the resistor using these readings. How does this value of resistance compare to the value obtained in part **c**? Can you explain the difference?

---

3 The graphs below show how the current through an electrical component varies with the voltage across it. The components used to obtain these graphs were:

- an LED
- a filament lamp
- a thermistor.

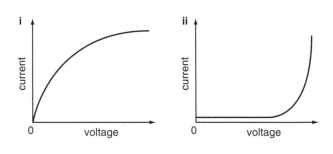

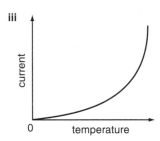

a Write down which graph **i**, **ii** or **iii** corresponds to each component.

b Describe how the resistance of a thermistor varies with temperature.

c Suggest a use for a thermistor.

4

a Describe how the resistance of a light-dependent resistor (LDR) varies with the light level.

b Suggest a use for an LDR.

2.1 Turning forces

Key points

- Moment of a force = force × perpendicular distance from pivot
- For a balanced system, sum of clockwise moments = sum of anticlockwise moments.

---

1 A student carried out a balancing experiment to find the weight of a lump of Plasticine. The apparatus is shown below. The metre rule is balanced.

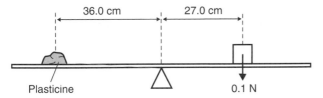

36.0 cm   27.0 cm

Plasticine   0.1 N

a Use the information on the diagram to calculate the weight of the Plasticine. Show your working.

b If you were carrying out this experiment, explain what you would do to ensure that you obtained as accurate a final result as possible for the weight of the Plasticine.

---

2 The diagram below shows the apparatus used in a balancing experiment.

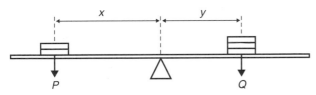

x   y

P   Q

a Before adding any weights, the student found that the metre rule did not quite balance when the pivot was on the 50.0 cm mark. What would you do in this case?

The loads used were 0.1 N slotted weights, as shown in the diagram.

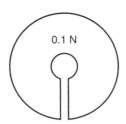

0.1 N

b Draw a diagram to show how you would place a slotted weight on the metre rule to take an accurate reading of its position.

c The table below shows some of the results that the student obtained.

P in ___	Q in ___	x in ___	y in ___	P x in ___	Q y in ___
0.2	0.4	40.0	20.0		
0.5	0.6	24.0		12.0	
0.4	0.7	35.0			

Copy and complete the table by adding the correct units and results.

IDEAS AND EVIDENCE

3 In 1995 a bridge was built across a river in the foothills of the Himalayas. There was road access from one side only so the bridge had to be built out from that side, as shown in the diagram.

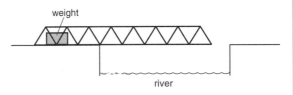

weight

river

Engineers first made a model to test their ideas. Each triangular section of the bridge model weighed 50 N. The diagram shows 15 sections bolted together.

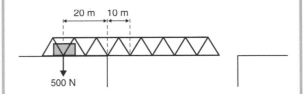

20 m   10 m

500 N

a At this stage of building, will the bridge topple into the river? Show your working.

b Two more sections must be added to reach the other side of the river.

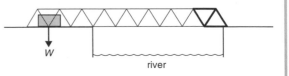

W

river

Is this possible without increasing the additional weight, W? Show your working.

2.2 Motion graphs

Key points

- Speed = $\dfrac{\text{distance travelled}}{\text{time taken}}$
- A distance–time graph shows how the distance travelled varies with time.
- The gradient of a distance–time graph is equal to the speed.

- A speed–time graph shows how the speed varies with time.
- The area under a speed–time graph is equal to the distance travelled.

1 Describe briefly what each of the graphs below show about the motion of a vehicle.

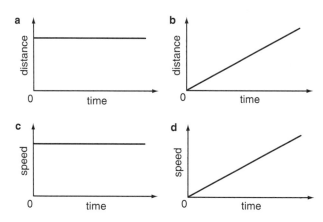

2 The table below represents the journey of a cyclist. Use the values to plot a distance–time graph.

time in s	distance in m
0	0
10	4
20	8
30	12
40	16
50	20
60	24
70	24
80	24

a Use the graph to calculate the speed of the cyclist over the first 50 seconds.

b Describe what the graph shows after the first 60 seconds.

3 Draw a sketch graph of distance against time for a bus that approaches a bus stop, waits at the stop for a while and then sets off again.

4 The following is a list of speeds:

- 0.2 m/s
- 2.0 m/s
- 10 m/s
- 50 m/s
- 100 m/s
- 500 m/s
- 1000 m/s
- 5000 m/s

Which of the above is a good estimate of the speed of:

a an aeroplane

b an Olympic 100 metre sprinter

c an express train

d normal walking speed?

5 The graph of speed against time shown below represents the journey of a lorry along a main road.

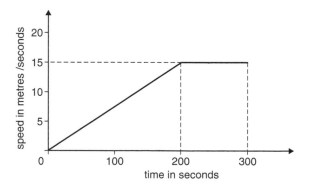

a What is happening to the speed of the lorry during the first 200 seconds?

b What is happening to the speed of the lorry during the next 100 seconds?

c Use the graph to calculate the distance travelled by the lorry in 300 seconds.

2.3 Displacement and velocity

Key points

- Displacement is a distance in a particular direction.
- Velocity is speed in a particular direction; it describes the speed and direction of a moving object.

- Velocity = $\dfrac{\text{displacement}}{\text{time}}$
- The gradient of a displacement–time graph is equal to velocity.
- Velocity is always measured in m/s when used in equations.

---

1 Distance and displacement do not mean the same thing. Explain the difference.

2 Speed and velocity do not mean the same thing. Explain the difference.

3 The displacement–time graph below shows the start of a sprinter's race.

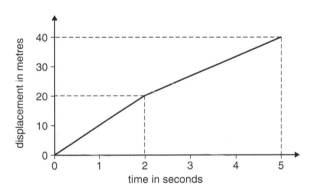

Use the graph to calculate:

a the velocity during the first 2 seconds

b the velocity during the next 3 seconds

c how far up the 100 metre track the sprinter has run in the first 5 seconds of the race.

4 Copy and complete the following table.

displacement in m	time in s	velocity in _____
150	15.0	
1480	32.0	
	26.4	24.0
792		13.2

---

5 A swimmer is swimming in a competition pool, 25 metres long. She swims to one end, turns and starts to swim back towards the start.

a Following the turn and after swimming 10 metres back towards the start, what distance has she swum?

b At the point described in part **a**, what is her displacement?

c Sketch a displacement–time graph to show her progress in the 10 metres before and after the turn (assume constant speed).

---

6 A toy truck was released from the top of a sloping track. Electronic timers recorded the time taken for the truck to travel each 0.4 metres down the track.

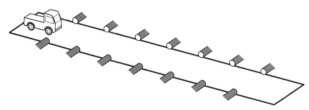

The readings obtained are shown in the table below.

displacement in m	time in s
0	0
0.4	0.80
0.8	1.12
1.2	1.38
1.6	1.64
2.0	1.78
2.4	1.96

a Plot a displacement–time graph of the readings. Draw the best-fit line.

b What does the shape of the line tell you about the motion of the truck?

2.4 Acceleration

Key points

- Acceleration = $\dfrac{\text{change in velocity}}{\text{time taken}}$
- The gradient of a velocity–time graph is equal to acceleration.

- Gravity gives all falling objects close to the Earth an acceleration of $10\,\text{m/s}^2$.

---

1 A car advertisement might say '0 to 60 in 15 seconds'.

a What, in more scientific terms, does this information tell you about?

b Would you prefer a car that was advertised as '0 to 60 in 10 seconds'? Explain your answer.

2

a A car changes its velocity from 7 m/s to 13 m/s over a period of 4 s. Calculate its acceleration.

b A cyclist changed velocity from 2 m/s to 4 m/s in 12 s. Calculate the acceleration.

c The cyclist had an instrument on his bicycle that displayed his acceleration. If the display read '–0.65', what would this tell you about the motion of the bicycle?

3 Copy and complete the following table.

starting velocity in m/s	finishing velocity in m/s	time in s	acceleration in _____
0	20	40	
0	15.5	25	
0.6	1.4		0.4
26	15	1.2	

4 A car is travelling at a speed of 31 m/s on a motorway. The driver takes her foot off the accelerator and the car takes 6.4 s to slow to 27 m/s.

a Calculate the deceleration.

b The car then begins to descend a long hill and the speed gradually builds back up to 31 m/s. If the acceleration is $0.125\,\text{m/s}^2$, how long does it take to speed up from 27 m/s to 31 m/s?

5 The graph below shows the motion of a skateboarder going downhill.

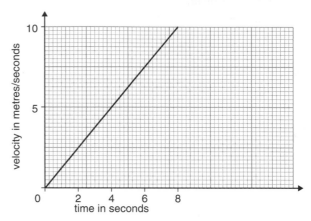

a From the graph, calculate the acceleration of the skateboarder. Show your working.

b Copy the graph, but continue the time axis up to 16 seconds. On the graph, draw lines to show the skateboarder:

  i slowing from 10 m/s to 6 m/s in 2 seconds
  ii then continuing at 6 m/s for 2 seconds
  iii then slowing to a halt in a further 4 seconds.

c Calculate the deceleration of the skateboarder in the final 4 seconds.

---

6 A cheetah can reach a speed of 30 m/s from a standing start in 5 seconds. A stationary aircraft at the end of a runway can take 30 seconds to reach a take-off speed of 60 m/s.

a Calculate the acceleration of the cheetah.

b Calculate the acceleration of the aircraft.

c Comment on the different accelerations.

---

7 Drag racing cars are designed to cover only short distances, but to do so in a very short time. From a standing start, a drag racing car can travel 500 m in a time of 8 seconds, reaching a velocity of 150 m/s.

a Calculate the average velocity of the car over 8 seconds.

b What is the acceleration of the car?

2.5 Forces

Key points

- A force is essentially a push or a pull.
- When an object A pulls or pushes an object B, object B pulls or pushes object A with an equal-sized force in the opposite direction (Newton's Third Law).
- Newton stated that there is a force of gravitational attraction between all objects.
- Weight = mass × gravitational field strength

1 Some parts of a bicycle are designed to make use of the force of friction. Other parts require friction to be reduced as much as possible.

a Suggest parts of a bicycle that are designed to make use of friction. Briefly explain each one.

b Name two parts of a bicycle where you would try to reduce the force of friction. How would you reduce the friction?

2 An astronaut was weighed before taking off for the Moon. His weight (including the spacesuit) was 1050 N.

a Calculate the mass of the astronaut and spacesuit (gravitational field strength = 10 N/kg).

b On the Moon, the gravitational field strength is 1.6 N/kg. Calculate the weight of the astronaut and spacesuit on the Moon.

3 The illustration below shows a boy stepping off a boat on to a landing stage.

a Describe what will happen next. Explain your prediction in terms of the forces acting.

b It would be sensible to secure the boat to the landing stage with a rope before stepping off. What force in the rope will keep the boat in position?

4 Copy and complete the following table to give an example of each type of force. The first one has been done for you.

type of force	example
weight	the attraction between a falling tennis ball and the Earth
tension	
lift	
friction	
air resistance	
reaction force	

5 The following is a list of forces:

- 0.001 N
- 20 N
- 5000 N
- 1 N
- 800 N
- 500 000 N
- 10 N

Match a value of force to each of the descriptions that follow. Each force value may be used once, more than once or not at all.

a the weight of an apple

b the weight of a 2 kg bag of sugar

c the weight of a man

d the weight of an insect

e the frictional force required to stop a car.

IDEAS AND EVIDENCE

6 American astronauts who went to the Moon developed a method of moving about which involved small jumps rather than walking.

Why do you think they found it so difficult to walk normally as they did on the Earth?

2.6 Force and motion

Key points

- The way in which an object moves in a straight line depends on the size and direction of the resultant force acting on it.
- When the forces on an object are balanced, the object is at rest or moving with constant velocity.
- When the forces on an object are unbalanced, the object is accelerating or decelerating.
- Good design reduces the resistance to motion so that objects can go faster.

1 A family travelled from Nottingham to Dover to begin their summer holiday. The car completed the journey using less than a full tank of petrol.

The next year, the family took two bicycles on the car's roof rack. The car needed refuelling before reaching Dover.

a Explain carefully why the bicycles on the roof rack caused the car to require more fuel for the same journey.

b Suggest a way of carrying the bicycles without increasing the fuel consumption so much.

2 Comment on the magnitude and direction of the resultant force in the following cases:

a a space probe travelling from the Earth to Neptune is moving a constant velocity

b a train travelling due North is slowing down

c a car travelling on a straight road is accelerating

d a lift starts ascending

e a car is travelling at 70 mph along a straight section of motorway.

3 A student pushes a heavy box across a carpet. The box moves at a constant velocity. The box moves off the carpet on to a tiled floor. The student continues to push with the same force and the box speeds up.

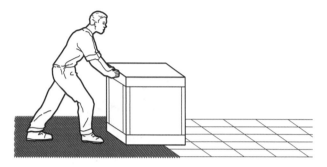

a Use your knowledge of forces to explain the movement of the box over the carpet and the tiled floor.

b When the box was pushed across the carpet the force of friction was 180 N. What was the force used by the student to push the box?

c When the box was pushed across the tiled floor the force of friction was 110 N. Calculate the resultant force on the box.

IDEAS AND EVIDENCE

4 Visitors to the Science Museum are often surprised that the Lunar Landing Module, used by American astronauts to land on the Moon, is box-shaped, with no attempt at streamlining, and with legs that appear hardly strong enough to support the weight of the module and astronauts inside.

Explain why, with a good understanding of the forces involved, you would not be surprised about the lack of streamlining or the weak appearance of the structure.

2.7 Force and acceleration

Key points

H Newton's Second Law states that the resultant force on an object is proportional to its mass times its acceleration.

H The newton is defined so that 'force = mass (in kg) × acceleration (in m/s^2)'.

H Car seat belts and crumple zones reduce the deceleration of the people in a car if there is an accident. This reduces the force acting on them, so they are less likely to be seriously injured.

H The equation, force = mass × acceleration, can also be applied to explain good techniques in a variety of sports.

---

1 The diagram below shows the crumple zones in a car.

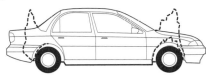

Describe how the crumple zones will help to protect the passengers in the event of a crash. Your answer should include the following words:

- force
- deceleration
- time.

2 Bungee jumpers rely on the stretchiness of the bungee rope. Explain why this is so important.

3 A group of students carried out a series of experiments using a trolley that was pulled down a track using different forces.

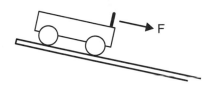

a The track was 'friction compensated'. What does this mean?

The results of their experiments are shown in the tables below.

Trolley mass = 1 kg

force in N	acceleration in m/s^2
0.5	48
1.0	94
1.5	145
2.0	190

Trolley mass = 2 kg

force in N	acceleration in m/s^2
0.5	24
1.0	50
1.5	74
2.0	95

b Taking into account possible small experimental errors, what can you conclude about the relationship between force and acceleration from the first table? Give some examples to justify your answer.

c What can you conclude about the relationship between mass and acceleration from the second table? Give some examples to justify your answer.

---

4 Copy and complete the following table.

force in N	mass in kg	acceleration in _____
	4.5	1.5
50	2.3	
650	450	
1500		0.8

5 Study the graph below. It shows the results of an experiment in which a 1 kg trolley was pulled down a track using different-sized forces.

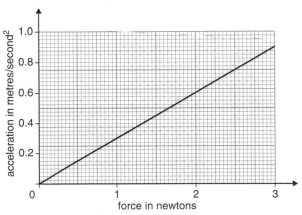

a What does the graph tell you about the relationship between force and acceleration?

b Copy the graph and draw an additional line to show the result you would expect if the experiment were repeated with the same conditions, except using a 2 kg trolley.

2.8 Force and energy

Key points

- Work done = force × distance moved in the direction of the force.
- Energy is the ability to do work.
- Work done = energy transferred by a force.
- Power = $\dfrac{\text{work done (or energy transferred)}}{\text{time taken}}$

- Weight = mass × gravitational field strength.
- Change in gravitational potential energy = mass × gravitational field strength × height moved (mgh)
- Kinetic energy = $\frac{1}{2}$ mass × (velocity)^2 ($\frac{1}{2}mv^2$)

---

1 Calculate the work done in each of the following situations:

a a fork-lift truck lifts a 6000 N load from ground level up to a shelf 3.0 m high

b a girl pushes her bicycle for 50 m along a pavement using an average force of 50 N

c a man, mass 85 kg, climbs up a ladder until he is 3.5 m above the ground

d a crane lifts a concrete floor section of mass 550 kg from the ground to a position 6.5 m high.

2 A boy climbs a flight of steps. There are 15 steps and each step is 0.20 m high. He takes 3.5 seconds to reach the top. The boy's mass is 60 kg.

0.20 m

a What is his weight?

b How much work does he do?

c Calculate his power.

3 An astronaut has a mass of 85 kg.

a What is his weight on the Earth?

b What would his weight be on the Moon?

c What would his weight be in outer space?

4 A Bonfire Night rocket, mass 0.15 kg, was launched from a plastic tube set in the ground. The rocket took off vertically at a velocity of 5 m/s.

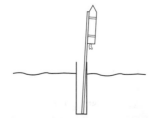

a Calculate the kinetic energy of the rocket just after take-off.

b Assuming that the mass of the rocket did not change during flight, what is the gain in gravitational potential energy from launch to its highest point?

c In practice the mass of the rocket does change because the fuel is used up. Do you think the actual highest point reached will be less than, more than or the same as the value calculated in part **b**?

d Explain your answer to part **c**.

---

5 The diagram shows part of a bagatelle board. The spring is compressed and then released to propel the marble.

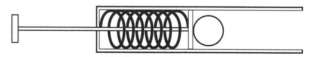

To compress the spring a force on the handle of 2.5 N was required to pull it back a distance of 0.12 m. The marble had a mass of 0.0375 kg.

a Calculate the work done in compressing the spring.

b Assuming that all the energy stored in the spring was transferred to kinetic energy of the marble, calculate the velocity of the marble as it was released.

c If the bagatelle board was 0.80 m above the floor and the marble dropped off the board on to the floor, what would be the loss in gravitational potential energy?

2.9 On the road

Key points

- The 'thinking distance' is how far you travel between seeing a hazard and applying the brakes. The 'thinking time' is less than 1 s but a fast car can travel quite a distance in that time.
- The distance a vehicle travels while braking is affected by the road surface as well as the mass and speed of the vehicle.
- Kinetic energy transferred = braking force × distance.
- Stopping distance = thinking distance + braking distance.
- The greater the speed, the greater the thinking distance *and* the greater the braking distance.

1 The stopping distance for a car depends on the 'thinking distance' and the 'braking distance'.

a Copy and complete this equation:

stopping distance = _____ + _____

b Assuming that a car is properly maintained so that its brakes and tyres are in good order, what three things does the braking distance depend on?

c Assuming that the driver is concentrating properly and that visibility is good, what three things might increase the driver's reaction time?

2 The graph below shows the change in speed of a car plotted against distance travelled. The distance is measured from the moment the driver sees a traffic light at red.

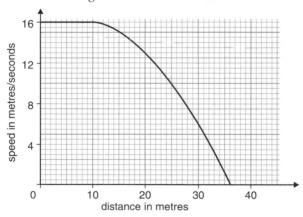

a Use the graph to find the thinking distance and the braking distance.

b Calculate the stopping distance.

c The mass of the car and driver is 875 kg. Calculate the kinetic energy when the car is travelling at 16 m/s.

d What is the work done as the car slows from 16 m/s to 0 m/s?

e Calculate the average braking force.

3 The graph below shows the change in speed and distance travelled by a car. The point at which the driver sees a traffic light at red is marked.

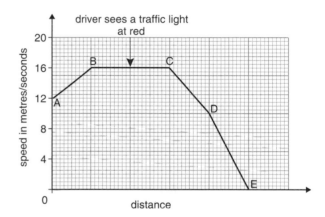

a State which part of the graph shows:

  i the end of the thinking distance
  ii the end of the braking distance
  iii a section where the car is accelerating.

b Calculate the maximum kinetic energy of the car and its driver (total mass = 850 kg).

4 The speed of a car is 15 m/s. At that speed the braking distance is 20 m and the thinking distance is 9 m.

a What is the stopping distance?

The speed is increased to 30 m/s.

b What is the new braking distance?

c What is the new stopping distance?

d If the mass of the car is 950 kg, what is its kinetic energy when travelling at 30 m/s?

2.10 **How things fall**

Key points

- When falling through a fluid (liquid or gas) the molecules of the fluid resist the motion so the acceleration is less.
- The greater the speed, the greater the resistive force.

- When the resistive force is equal to the weight of the object its velocity becomes constant; this is called terminal velocity.
- Gravity gives all falling objects close to the Earth an acceleration of 10 m/s².

1 The diagram below shows a free fall parachutist.

a Copy the diagram and show clearly these two forces: the parachutist's weight and air resistance.

b Explain carefully why, before the parachute is opened, the parachutist will reach a terminal velocity.

c Explain carefully what happens to the parachutist when the parachute opens. (Include in your answers the words 'weight', 'air resistance' and 'terminal velocity'.)

2 On a day when there was no wind, a scientist dropped a snooker ball and large sheet of card from the top of a tall building.

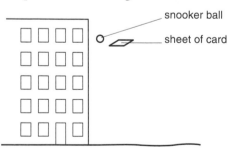

snooker ball

sheet of card

a Describe how you would expect the two objects to move through the air. Which would you expect to reach the ground first?

b Explain your answer to part **a**, using the words 'terminal velocity', 'air resistance', 'accelerate' and 'weight'.

c If the piece of card had been folded to a simple aeroplane shape, would it have moved through the air any differently? Explain your answer.

3 An astronaut on the Moon dropped a geological hammer and a feather from the same height and at the same time.

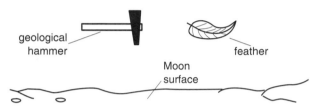

geological hammer

feather

Moon surface

a What did the astronaut notice about the motion of the two objects?

b How would the results of this experiment differ if it were repeated on the Earth?

4 A student carried out some experiments to study the terminal velocity of a steel ball falling through different liquids. For each test, the ball was dropped from a height of 50 cm above the liquid surface. The liquid was contained in a narrow transparent glass tube. The times at which the steel ball passed fixed points on the tube were recorded automatically. The liquids used were water, motor oil, cooking oil and Golden Syrup.

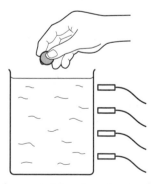

a What are the variables that the student studied in this experiment?

b What possible variables had to be kept constant during the experiment?

c Draw a sketch graph of velocity against time to show the type of result you would expect to see when using motor oil.

2.11 **Keeping warm**

Key points

- Conduction occurs mainly in solids.
- Convection transfers energy from hot to cold areas by fluid movement in liquids and gases.

- Radiation can travel through a vacuum; it is the way in which heat reaches us from the Sun.
- Domestic insulation reduces energy transfer by conduction, convection and radiation.

---

1 The diagram below shows a cross-section of a domestic refrigerator.

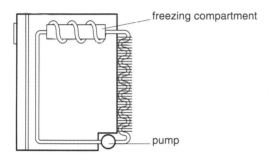

a Explain why the freezing compartment is near the top of the fridge.

b Explain why it would not be a good idea to replace the plastic-coated wire shelves with solid plastic shelves.

c The cooling fins at the back of the refrigerator are made of metal and painted black.

  i Why are they made of metal?

  ii Why are they painted black?

---

2 The diagram below shows a vacuum flask.

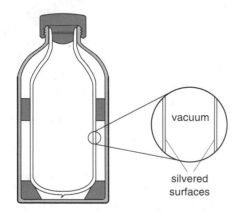

a Which type of heat transfer is reduced by the silvered surfaces? Explain your answer.

b Which type/types of heat transfer is/are reduced by the vacuum? Explain your answer.

c The plastic screw-in stopper reduces heat transfer by conduction and convection. Explain how heat would be lost by convection if the stopper were left off.

---

3 On hot summer days the land near the coast is warmer than the sea. At night, when the sky is clear, the land can cool more quickly than the sea. These effects cause on-shore and off-shore breezes.

a Copy and complete the diagram above to show an on-shore breeze.

b State whether this occurs in the day or at night.

c Explain your answer in terms of convection.

d Repeat steps in **a**, **b** and **c** to explain an off-shore breeze.

---

4 Fibre glass is a better conductor of heat than air is. Explain why a hot water tank will lose heat more slowly if it is fitted with a fibre glass jacket than if it is just surrounded by air.

---

5 The diagram below shows an experiment that demonstrates that water is a bad conductor of heat but transfers heat well by convection.

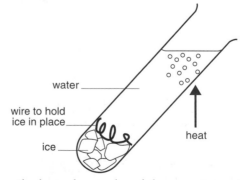

Describe how the results of the experiment lead to the conclusion indicated above.

2.12 Energy efficiency

Key points

- Energy efficiency = $\dfrac{\text{useful energy output}}{\text{total energy input}}$
- All machines waste energy, often as heat due to friction, but good design should make them as efficient as possible.

- Energy becomes degraded when it is spread over such a large area that no further use can be made of it.
- It is important to heat buildings efficiently so that little energy is wasted and fuel bills are kept as low as possible.

1 A crane lifts a concrete block at a building site. The block weighs 1000 kg and is lifted through a height of 15 m.

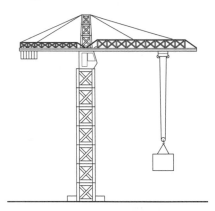

a Calculate the work done on the load.

b The time taken to raise the concrete block is 24 s. Calculate the power output of the crane's motor.

c The motor is 25% efficient. Calculate the power input to the motor.

2

a Copy and complete the following table.

device	useful energy output in J	energy input in J	energy efficiency
A	300	375	
B		60	0.033
C	8		0.8

b By considering the energy input and energy output, state which device (A, B or C) is:

  i a domestic light bulb

  ii a pulley system lifting a 300 N load through a distance of 1 m

  iii a catapult.

3 To have a conversation with a friend, you must be reasonably close together. Even a shouted conversation is very difficult at more than about 10 metres apart.

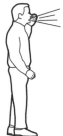

a Explain this in terms of the degradation of energy.

b What is used to make conversations over long distances possible?

c Explain, in terms of energy changes and energy efficiency, how the device described in part **b** enables long distance conversations to be possible.

4 Consider a bicycle dynamo.

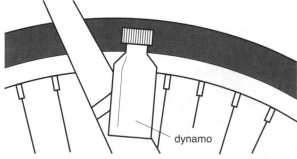

dynamo

The dynamo is less than 100% efficient. Suggest as many parts as you can where energy is wasted. Briefly explain each one.

5 An athlete is running in a race. About 10% of the energy the athlete uses is useful energy output, moving him towards the finishing post.

a Where does the athlete get his energy from?

b Suggest why the efficiency is as low as 10%.

c In what forms is energy wasted?

3.1 What are waves?

Key points

- Waves are caused by vibrations.
- Waves transfer energy from one place to another without transferring matter.

- There are two types of wave:
  longitudinal wave
  transverse wave.

1 List six different objects that produce sound.

For each one,

a write down what is oscillating, and

b what happens as the sound energy is transferred from the object to your ears.

c How could you make each sound louder?

2 There is a speed limit of 2.5 m/s for canal boats on parts of the canal system. This speed limit controls the size of the waves created by the boats and protects the canal banks. Because the canals are narrow, the wave from the bow of a boat moves along with the boat.

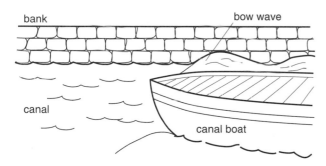

Draw a sketch to show how the water from a single wave moves as the wave moves along the bank. Show how this movement of the water damages the bank.

3 'Slinky' springs are used by teachers to demonstrate both transverse and longitudinal waves.

a Explain how this is achieved.

b What are the differences between the types of waves?

c Write down two examples of each type of wave.

d Explain the meaning of i frequency, ii wavelength and iii amplitude.

4 If your hotel room is above the disco it will be quite noisy. Explain the ways that the sound of the disco can be transferred from the disco into your room (there are at least three).

5

a Assume that the boat in question **2** produces a bow wave whose energy is moving forwards with the same speed as the boat. If the wave has a wavelength of 1 m, what is the frequency of the wave?

b Estimate the potential energy of the water in the wave on one side of the canal boat if the distance between the boat and the bank is 1 m and the amplitude of the wave is 15 cm. Then find a rough value for the power dissipated at the bank. Use $g = 10$ N/kg.

Hint: Assume that the wave is part of a cylinder. The volume of a cylinder is $\pi r^2 h$ and the density of water is 1000 kg/m^3. You may have to increase the radius very slightly to allow for the sine shape of the wave.

6 Copy the diagram of the transverse wave shown below and continue it for two more waves. $\lambda = 8$ cm, $a = 1$ cm

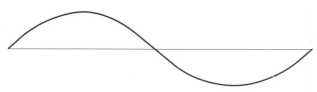

Underneath your diagram, draw a line with dots marked every centimetre. Measure the displacement of the transverse wave every centimetre and transfer this to the line you have drawn below, which represents the particles in a longitudinal wave. Upward displacement in the transverse wave becomes forward displacement in the longitudinal wave, and down becomes backwards. Mark the wavelength of the new longitudinal wave. Describe how the particles in the new wave move as the wave passes.

3.2 Wave characteristics

Key points

- Amplitude is the maximum displacement of a particle in a wave from its rest position.
- Frequency is the number of complete waves passing a point in one second.

- Wavelength is the distance between two successive points on a wave of similar displacement.
- Speed is a measure of how fast a wave is travelling.

1 Sam is watching waves entering a harbour.

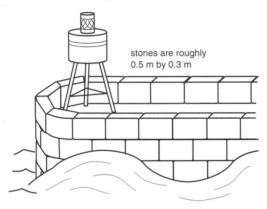

stones are roughly 0.5 m by 0.3 m

Write down how she could estimate:

a the amplitude of the waves

b the wavelength of the waves

c the frequency of the waves

d How could she then calculate the speed of the waves?

2 Waves in a swimming pool have a wavelength of 5 m and a frequency of 0.3 Hz.

a Calculate the speed of the waves.

Hint: You need to use the wave equation. Don't forget to give the unit.

b Explain why swimmers are not swept along by the waves.

3

a Dog whistles cannot be heard by humans. The frequency of the sound is well above the limit of human hearing. Suggest an experiment that you could do, without a dog, to show that the whistle actually works.

b How could you use the equipment from part **a** to measure the frequency of the sound wave from the dog whistle?

Hint: You may need to draw some sketches to explain what you are doing.

4

a Rumble strips on a road begin 0.5 m apart and decrease to 0.2 m apart. A motorist travelling at 30 m/s does not slow down. Use these figures to explain what the motorist hears. Use the word 'pitch' in your explanation.

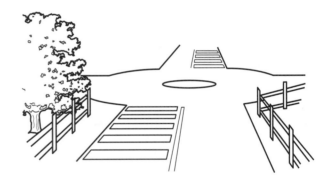

b On a concrete section of the main A1 road, motorists hear a high-pitched sound of about 1000 Hz coming from the surface of the road. Explain what might be happening.

5 Complete the following table:

wave	speed in m/s	frequency in Hz	wavelength in m
water	1.6	0.2	
sound		200	1.7
string	200		1.3
microwaves		1×10^{10}	3×10^{-2}
light	3×10^8		5×10^{-7}
radio waves	3×10^8	200×10^3	

6 Mobile phone aerials are half a wavelength long. How long will the aerial be for microwaves of frequency 9.4×10^9 Hz?

Hint: You will have to use the wave equation and know the speed of microwaves.

3.3 Water waves

Key points

- Water waves are an example of transverse waves.
- In the laboratory, water waves can be seen with the aid of a ripple tank.
- The water waves in a ripple tank model the behaviour of other types of wave.

1 Using a ripple tank, explain how you could produce:

a circular ripples

b a plane (straight) ripple

c a long wavelength continuous wave

d a short wavelength continuous wave.

2

a Draw a set of plane wavefronts and draw the ray that shows the direction of movement of the energy.

b Draw a set of circular wavefronts and draw a set of rays coming from the source of vibration.

c Explain how you could use the set of circular wavefronts to show that light energy from a small light bulb travels out in all directions.

3 Using words and drawings, explain the meaning of these keywords:

a concave

b convex

c converge

d diverge

e focus.

4 The reflector of a car headlamp is a special parabolic shape that always produces plane waves after reflection.

Draw the reflector twice.

a On your first drawing, draw a set of waves that come from the front of the bulb without being reflected.

b On your second drawing, draw a set of waves from the back of the bulb that are reflected from the reflector.

5

a Draw a set of circular wavefronts. The wave energy of these waves spreads out at the same speed in all directions.

b Now draw a set of waves that travel as fast as yours in one direction, but twice as fast in a direction perpendicular to this.

c Now try drawing a set of sound waves that are of a single frequency and produced by a large loudspeaker in a park. There the wind is blowing at 20 m/s from the right.

Hint: If you are careful you could try drawing this to scale. The speed of sound in air is 300 m/s.

d By looking at your drawing, suggest something that is happening to the sound that you hear in the park.

6 Water waves enter a small bay that is shaped like a reflector.

Apply what you know about waves to suggest where erosion is taking place and why the bay is this shape.

Hint: You need to know that waves slow down in shallow water.

7 A ripple tank has a vibrator that has a frequency of 50 Hz. A strobe illuminates the waves so that the wave pattern is stationary.

a What are the possible frequencies of the strobe? Explain why other frequencies are not possible.

b Explain what happens if the frequency of the strobe is increased slightly.

3.4 Reflection of light and sound

Key points

- Light is reflected from surfaces.
- A flat surface gives regular reflection.
- An uneven surface gives diffuse reflection.

- The angle of incidence equals the angle of reflection.
- Sound obeys the same rules of reflection as light.

1 Draw a plan diagram of a mirror.

a On your diagram draw the normal ray, the incident ray and the reflected ray. Mark the angles of incidence and reflection.

b Write down the relationship between the angle of incidence and the angle of reflection.

2

a Explain the following terms:

  i regular reflection
  ii diffuse reflection.

b Use the ideas of regular and diffuse reflection to explain why a room with a wood floor sounds noisier than one with a carpeted floor.

c Explain how an echo is formed in a large empty room.

d If a room is 30 m long, how long does it take for an echo to return? The speed of sound is 340 m/s.

3 Ann looks at herself in a mirror. She is 1.4 m tall.

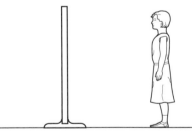

Draw a ray diagram which shows that she needs a mirror that is only 0.7 m high to see herself full length.

4 The door of an office has a window made up of strips of mirror with clear glass in between.

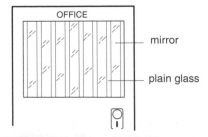

a Explain why it is possible to see out from inside the office but not possible to see in from outside the office.

b How would the situation change if the office light was on inside and it was dark outside?

5

a John stands by a reflector and speaks softly. Sarah hears everything he says. Why is this?

b What do you think Kate hears?

c Draw the ray diagram for the sound travelling from John to Sarah.

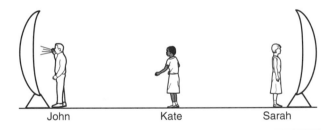

John   Kate   Sarah

6

a Explain how you can measure the speed of sound, using a wall as a mirror.

b Devise suitable distances and times to give a speed of sound in air of 340 m/s.

c Joe says that a hedge would do, instead of a wall. Is his suggestion sensible?

d Why would it be difficult to measure the speed of light with a similar type of experiment?

IDEAS AND EVIDENCE

7 James is at a theme park inside the dome waiting for the Cine2000 film to start. The dome is about 15 m high and 30 m across. He is standing near the screen, to one side, and can hear two people speaking quite clearly. Nobody near him is talking. Use a ray diagram to explain what is happening.

Hint: You will need to talk about the focusing of sound to explain this.

3.5 Refraction

Key points

- The speed of a wave changes when the wave passes from one material to another.

- This change in speed causes a change in wavelength and hence can cause a change in direction.
- This is called refraction.

1

a Explain the difference between reflection and refraction.

b Give two practical examples from real life of both reflection and refraction.

c Draw ray diagrams for both reflection and refraction, to explain what is happening.

2 Glass, plastic, water and air are all transparent. Glass is the most dense medium and air is the least dense. Put the four media, glass, plastic, water and air, in order so that in the first the light travels fastest and in the last it travels slowest.

3 Fill in the spaces in the following table. Use the formula from question **6**.

substance	refractive index	angle i in degrees	angle r in degrees
water	1.33	70	
	1.50		35
dense glass		74	30
plastic	1.42		40
		71	23

4 Cornfields warm up in sunshine, while lakes tend to stay cool.

a Copy and complete the diagram showing the wavefronts and rays to find out what happens to the sound.

b Would you rather have a cool lake or a warm cornfield between your house and a busy motorway? Would it be different at night?

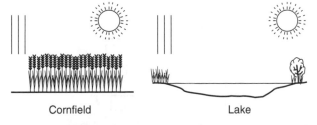

Cornfield   Lake

5 Who can hear the watch loudest? Finish the wavefronts and draw the rays to find out.

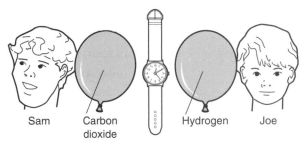

Sam   Carbon dioxide   Hydrogen   Joe

6

a Draw a diagram, showing a set of wavefronts representing a beam of light passing into a tank of water at 45° to the normal.

b The refractive index, n, of water is 1.33. On another diagram, similar to that in part a, draw the wavefronts accurately with the wavelength in air equal to 2 cm.

Hint: You need to use the formula:

sine (angle of incidence) = n × sine (angle of refraction)

7 When a ray passes through a parallel-sided glass block, it is displaced sideways by a perpendicular distance d.

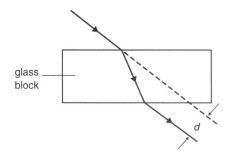

glass block

d

Draw ray diagrams for angle i equal to 20° and 80° and a glass block 4 cm thick. Measure d each time. What are the maximum and minimum values of d and do they depend upon the thickness of the glass block?

3.6 Images

Key points

- Images can be real or virtual.

- An image is formed when light is reflected or refracted.

1 Rays go to real images and come away from virtual images. So a virtual image cannot be projected on a surface but a real image can.

Make a list of the following images under the headings 'real' and 'virtual':

a at a cinema

b in a camera

c in the eye

d in a mirror

e a television picture

f in a magnifying glass

g in a microscope

h in binoculars

i image of a fish in water.

2 List the important features of an image in a mirror, for example where it is, what it is like, how it compares with the object.

3 Ann looks at her finger through a thick glass block. It looks normal. She then rotates the block slightly. What does she see then? Draw a diagram to illustrate your answer.

4 Explain what lateral inversion is.

5 Sam is not convinced that the image is behind a plane mirror. How would you explain this to her, using a few pins and a small mirror?

6 Kaleidoscope images. Copy the diagram below and finish it by drawing the other five sectors of the kaleidoscope.

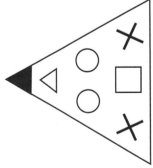

Now draw some more patterns of your own.

7

a Explain the terms 'real depth' and 'apparent depth'.

b Apply the terms 'real depth' and 'apparent depth' to the situation in which a small boy is looking at some coins that have been thrown into a wishing well which appears to be 90 cm deep. How deep are the coins. Will he get a surprise?

Hint: Use the equation

real depth = refractive index × apparent depth

The refractive index for water = 1.33.

8 When you are travelling in a train or car and look out of the side window, objects that are stationary seem to be moving relative to (past) one another. Explain how this phenomenon can be used to detect when two objects are at the same place. Explain how this method is used to locate accurately the position of a virtual image.

9 Copy the diagram of the games machine shown below and draw light rays on it to show the position of the image that the player sees. What are the practical advantages of this design.

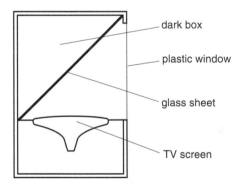

dark box

plastic window

glass sheet

TV screen

10 Carefully copy these pictures of bits of lenses. Plot the paths of the rays through them. Which is most likely to produce a real image and which will produce a virtual image?

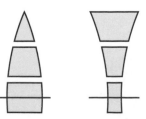

3.7 Diffraction

Key points

- Diffraction is the spreading out of a wave after it has passed through a gap or reached a corner.

- The amount of spreading depends on the size of the gap compared to the wavelength.
- A smaller gap produces more diffraction.

1

a Explain what is meant by diffraction. Illustrate your explanation by copying and completing these wavefront diagrams of water waves.

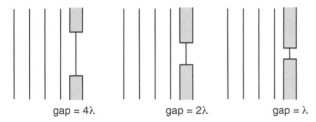

gap = 4λ   gap = 2λ   gap = λ

b What happens if the gap is much smaller than the wavelength?

2 Explain why Peter can hear Jane but he cannot see her.

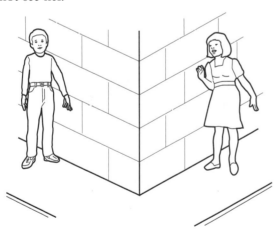

3 Pat says that the diffraction of light is evidence of its wave nature. Explain what she means. Does this also apply to waves like sound and ripples on a pond? Illustrate your answer with some examples.

4 Answer these questions with reference to the concept of diffraction.

a Your stereo is playing loudly in your room and you have the bass boost on. Explain why when you leave the room it is the higher pitched sounds that you hear more clearly.

b The tweeters on your hi-fi are quite small and the woofers are quite large. Why is this? Would having very large tweeters affect the distribution of sound around the room? (Low frequencies are approx. 30 Hz; high frequencies are approx. 3000 Hz.)

c Explain why cars need outside aerials to receive FM radio signals of frequency 100 MHz. The speed of sound is 3×10^8 m/s.

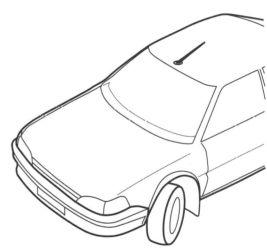

d A microwave oven has a metal grid inside the window which has small holes all over it. Explain why you can see into the oven but the microwaves do not get out.

Hint: You need to know that the wavelength of microwaves is a few centimetres and the wavelength of light less than a micrometre.

5 The table below shows information about water waves, sound waves, light waves and radio waves. Copy the table and fill in the gaps.

wave	wavelength in cm	gap size for diffraction in cm
	100	
		500
	1×10^5	
		6×10^{-5}

4.1 The electromagnetic spectrum

Key points

- Electromagnetic waves are transverse waves.

- All waves in the electromagnetic spectrum travel at the speed of light 300 000 000 m/s (usually written as 3×10^8 m/s).

1

a Write down, in order of increasing wavelength, the parts of the complete electromagnetic spectrum.

b Write down the colours that occur naturally in nature, for example a red sunset. Explain how these colours occur.

c Draw and colour a continuous spectrum for light. Put in the regions where ultraviolet and infrared radiation occur.

d Explain why we say that the spectrum is continuous.

2 The diagram below shows the waveform of yellow light. Copy the diagram twice. On one copy, draw the waveforms for blue light and red light. On the other copy, draw waveforms for ultraviolet and infrared radiation.

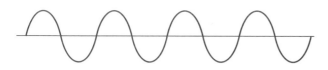

3

a You are given a prism and a bright source of light. Describe how you would produce a clear visible spectrum on a piece of white card.

b Newton performed an experiment where he put an upturned prism in a spectrum that he had just produced. Draw a diagram to show what happened.

c Newton also took one of the colours from his spectrum and allowed it to pass through another prism. Explain what you think happened.

4 A TV screen is covered with red, blue and green phosphors. These produce light when they are hit from behind by electrons.

a How are the different colours in a TV picture produced?

b How is the brightness of the colours controlled?

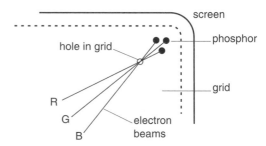

IDEAS AND EVIDENCE

5 In 1905 Einstein proposed that light waves were made up of small units of energy called photons. He said the energy of these photons could be calculated by multiplying the frequency of the light wave by the Planck constant, 6.63×10^{-34} J s.

Using the wavelength information for the different colours, calculate:

a the approximate frequency of the colours

b the energy of the photons.

Copy and complete the table below.

colour	wavelength in m	frequency in Hz	photon energy in J
violet	400×10^{-9}		
blue	460×10^{-9}		
green	550×10^{-9}		
orange	610×10^{-9}		
red	660×10^{-9}		

c What happens to the energy as the wavelength of the light decreases?

4.2 Infrared and ultraviolet

Key points

- Infrared radiation has wavelengths longer than visible light, up to nearly 1 mm.
- Infrared radiation is produced by warm or hot objects.
- Ultraviolet radiation has wavelengths shorter than visible light, typically 1×10^{-8} m.
- Ultraviolet radiation is produced by very hot objects.

1 List the sources of radiant heat in your house. You will probably be able to find about ten.

Hint: Think of the things that get hot but don't look hot. Describe what is happening in four of them.

2 Explain how the surfaces of the cans of water shown below affect how fast the cans of water heat up.

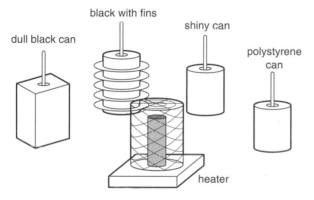

3 Draw infrared rays from the heater to the blackened thermometer. Explain what you think will happen when the heater is switched on.

4

a Explain what is meant by 'a sunscreen has a sun protection factor of 20'?

b How much longer could you stay in the sunshine using a factor 20 sunscreen compared to using a factor 5 sunscreen if the burn time for that day was 20 minutes?

c Why might these times change for a person with a darker skin?

5 The diagram shows how the infrared rays produced by plants from sunlight are trapped inside a greenhouse. Draw this diagram and explain why the greenhouse continues to warm up and can become very hot.

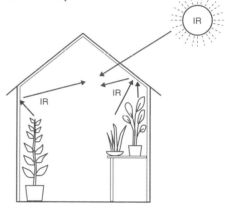

6 A fluorescent bulb is about five times as efficient as a conventional light bulb. Work out the power of the fluorescent bulbs that would produce the same amount of light as normal 40 W, 60 W and 100 W conventional bulbs.

7 The diagram below shows what happens inside a fluorescent tube. Copy the diagram and use the information to explain how the tube works.

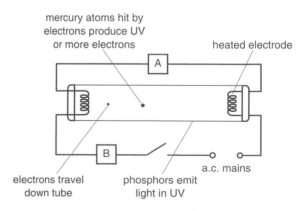

A bimetallic strip opens in the starter, A, and switches off the current through the large inductance, B. A large voltage is induced across the tube that starts the discharge.

4.3 Opposite ends (1)

Key points

- At one end of the electromagnetic spectrum, next to infrared, are radio waves.
- Radio waves have wavelengths that range from a few centimetres to nearly two kilometres.
- Within the radio waveband are microwaves, radar and the more familiar radio and television waves.

- At the opposite end of the spectrum, next to ultraviolet, is the X-ray waveband.
- X-rays have wavelengths that are shorter than 1×10^{-9} m.
- The X-ray waveband includes very penetrating, energetic, gamma rays with even shorter wavelengths.

1 Explain how microwaves are used in:

a cooking
b mobile telephone communication
c receiving weather satellite images.

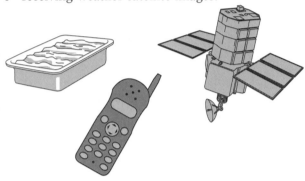

2 Copy out the passage below about microwave communication. Use the following words to fill in the gaps.

band width	hours
conversation	line of sight
curvature	radio
delay	towers
geostationary	travel

The microwave band is used for communications because it has a large _____. Unlike _____ waves, microwaves cannot be broadcast. A microwave link needs a _____. Microwave transmitters and receivers are normally mounted on tall _____ so that the beam is not interrupted by buildings or the _____ of the Earth. One problem for satellite communications, is the time it takes for a signal to _____ up to the satellite and back down again. A _____ satellite, which orbits the earth every 24 _____ would need to be 36 000 km above the Earth's surface. This causes a noticeable _____, which can be awkward in a _____.

3 The main frequency bands in the radio spectrum are listed below on the left. Match them to the frequencies listed below on the right.

very high frequency	30 kHz–300 kHz
ultra high frequency	300 kHz–3 MHz
microwaves	3 MHz–30 MHz
medium frequency	30 MHz–300 MHz
low frequency	300 MHz–3 GHz
high frequency	above 3 GHz

Put this information in a table and say what each band is used for.

4 The house in the drawing is in a remote valley. TV and mobile phone reception have been improved by the installation of a repeater on the hill behind the house. All transmissions come from the west. It is evening and the Sun is setting in the west.

Copy the picture and draw beams of wavefronts to show what happens to the following radiations: light, IR, microwaves, short-wavelength radio waves (FM) and long-wavelength radiowaves, all coming from the west.

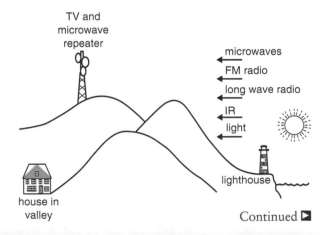

Continued ▶

4.3 Opposite ends (2)

5 X-rays are used in medicine to diagnose broken bones.

a Explain how the X-rays are used, how the information is recorded and why it is possible to see the broken bone. Draw what you might see.

b List the safety precautions that must be taken whilst using X-rays.

6

a Explain how syringes that are made for use in hospitals can be sterilised by gamma rays after they have been packed in sealed plastic bags.

b What are the advantages of this type of sterilisation?

A similar technique is used to sterilise fruit and vegetables so that they remain in good condition for much longer. Some consumer groups are worried about doing this and say that food like this must be labelled clearly so that shoppers know that it has been irradiated.

c What are the advantages and disadvantages of irradiating food in this way?

7 Low, medium and high frequency radio waves both travel across the surface of the Earth and are reflected from the lower surface of ionised layers in the atmosphere about 100 km from the ground.

a A transmitter produces a 'surface wave' and a 'sky wave'. If the glancing angle of the sky wave at the bottom of an ionised layer is about 30°, the wave will be reflected back to the ground. Draw a diagram to show what happens to the two waves.

b Explain how it is possible for there to be no signal where the two waves meet again on the ground.

8 Radioactive iodine, which decays releasing gamma rays, is used to find out about the activity of a patient's thyroid gland. The thyroid gland is located in the neck. The patient is given a compound containing the radioactive iodine and then, after a little while, the neck region is scanned with a g-m tube.

Explain what differences there might be between the scan of a normal thyroid gland and an overactive one.

9 Satellite images for weather forecasting are now taken using radar. Radar is more penetrating than light or infrared radiation and allows forecasters to see the state of the water inside the cloud.

a What is radar?

b How can radar help in forecasting bad weather?

10 Microwaves cause heating when absorbed by water. Explain why

a microwaves are used to cook and reheat food

b people are concerned about the safety of children who are constantly holding their mobile phones close to their ears.

11 Gamma rays are used to kill cancerous growths inside the body.

a Explain how this is done.

b Say how the damage to healthy cells is minimised.

12 Radio waves are more readily diffracted than microwaves. Explain why this makes them more suitable for broadcasting than microwaves.

13 Complete the table below about the parts of the electromagnetic spectrum.

radiation	produced by	detected by	uses
gamma rays	radioactive decay		
X-rays	electrons hitting a metal target		
UV radiation			
Light			
IR radiation	objects up to 500 °C		
microwaves	klystron oscillator		
radio waves		radio circuits	

4.4 Total internal reflection

Key points

- When light passes from a more dense into a less dense material the angle of refraction is greater than the angle of incidence.
- At some larger angles of incidence, the angle is too large for refraction to take place. The light remains in the material by reflecting off the boundary.
- Total internal reflection is used, amongst other things, for telecommunications and endoscopy.

1 Draw four ray diagrams for light passing from glass into air. Make the angle of incidence in the glass approximately 15°, 30°, 45° and 60°. The critical angle for glass is 42°.

2 The diagram below is of a totally internally reflecting prism.

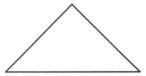

a Draw ray diagrams to show how this prism can be used to turn rays through 90° and 180°.

b What is the minimum refractive index for this prism to be able to turn a ray through 90°?

c Would a prism made of ice, refractive index 1.3, work like this?

d When you look into a prism at something behind you, is it the right way up? Draw a ray diagram to find out.

3

a Bubbles of air coming up through water appear silver because of light reflected off the top of the bubbles. Copy the diagram below (left) and draw rays to show the reflected light.

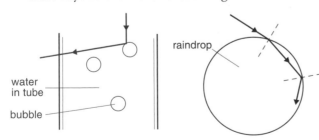

b A light ray entering the top of a raindrop is refracted and then totally internally reflected from the back of the drop. It is then refracted out of the bottom of the drop. Copy and finish the diagram above (right) to show what happens.

4 Optical fibres are used to transmit telephone messages over long distances. The main advantage is that digital signals can be used. The digital signals are produced by small lasers. The digital signals travel further than electric currents before they need to be amplified. The signal cannot be tapped, unlike a current in a wire, so the information is much safer. Although optical fibres do suffer from interference, it can be removed easily at the receiver.

a What is an optical fibre?

b How are digital signals different from analogue signals?

c Why are lasers used?

d Why is the information safer?

e How does removing interference affect the quality of the information in the message?

5 Draw a diagram to show how an endoscope works. What are the advantages of using endoscopes in medicine?

6 The critical angle depends on the refractive index of the transparent material. Complete the table below.

substance	refractive index	critical angle
water	1.33	
glass		42°
dense glass	1.92	
diamond	2.42	

Hint: Use the relationship 1/sine (critical angle) = refractive index, n

7

a Explain why digital signals in an optical fibre allow more rapid transmission of data than electric currents.

b Explain how several telephone messages can be sent along the same fibre at the same time.

4.5 Ultrasound

Key points

- There is a sound spectrum just as there is an electromagnetic spectrum.
- Ultrasound is very high frequency sound with a pitch too high for us to hear.

1

a What is the frequency range of human hearing?

b What, in terms of frequency, is meant by the term 'ultrasound'?

2 Delicate items can be cleaned using ultrasound.

a Give an example of an item that could be cleaned in this way.

b Explain, briefly, how the cleaning is carried out.

c Explain how the ultrasound causes dirt to be removed from the delicate item.

3 A ship sends out a pulse of ultrasound that is reflected off the seabed and detected back at the ship. It takes 0.9 s for the pulse to travel from the ship to the seabed and back to the ship. The speed of sound in sea water is 1500 m/s.

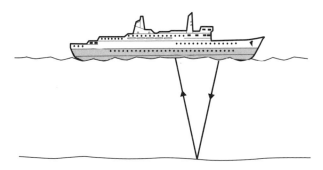

a What name is given to the reflected sound wave?

b Calculate the total distance that the pulse of ultrasound travels – from the ship to the seabed and back to the ship. Show your working.

c Calculate the depth of the seabed.

d What difference would be noticed in the time taken for the pulse to travel from the ship and back if the ship passed over a wreck on the seabed?

e Estimate the difference in the time taken for the pulse to travel from the ship and back as the ship passes over the wreck.

f Suggest why sound waves that are within the frequency range of normal human hearing are unsuitable for the type of use described above.

4 Very large containers are used in some industrial processes and it is necessary to monitor the depth of liquid in the containers. This can be done using pulses of ultrasound. The diagram below shows a container and a device that emits and receives ultrasound. Some of the ultrasound emitted is reflected back from the surface of the liquid.

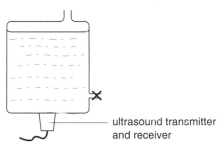

ultrasound transmitter and receiver

a Why is ultrasound used for this purpose rather than sound?

b What is meant by the term 'pulse'?

A pulse of ultrasound emitted is displayed on a cathode ray oscilloscope (CRO) screen. The reflected pulse is also displayed on the screen. The time base of the CRO is set at 1 ms/cm.

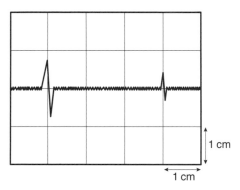

1 cm

1 cm

c Explain why the first pulse displayed on the CRO screen has greater amplitude than the second pulse.

d Calculate the time interval between the emission of the pulse and the reception of the reflected pulse.

e The speed of the ultrasound through the liquid is 1500 m/s. Calculate the depth of the liquid.

f The frequency of the ultrasound is 50 000 Hz. Calculate the wavelength of the ultrasound.

4.6 **Seismic waves**

Key points

H   Seismic waves are the shock waves caused by earthquakes.

H   Three types of wave are produced, called L, P and S.

H   L waves are surface waves travelling through the Earth's crust.

H   They can damage buildings because they cause the Earth's crust to move up and down.

H   P and S waves are body waves that pass through the body of the Earth.

H   This difference allows us to deduce the structure of the Earth.

1

a   Seismic waves are called L, P and S waves. State which is/are longitudinal waves and which are transverse waves.

Earthquakes produce wave motions inside the Earth. The diagrams below show a P wave and an S wave.

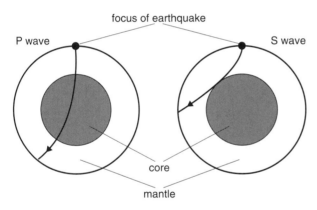

b   State whether P waves travel through solids or liquids or both.

c   State whether S waves travel through solids or liquids or both.

d   Explain how the movement of P waves and S waves through the Earth is evidence that supports the idea that the Earth has a layered structure, as shown in the diagrams.

2   Give the scientific terms that match the following descriptions.

a   The place where rocks break suddenly, causing earthquakes.

b   The origin of an earthquake.

c   The point on the Earth's surface immediately above the point of origin of an earthquake.

d   The name given to the three types of waves transmitted from the origin of an earthquake.

e   The surface waves that travel more slowly than the others waves and cause damage to buildings.

f   The waves that can travel through all parts of the Earth.

g   The waves that cannot travel through liquids.

h   The instrument that is used to detect waves on the surface of the Earth.

---

3   The diagram below shows the structure of the Earth. The epicentre of an earthquake is marked.

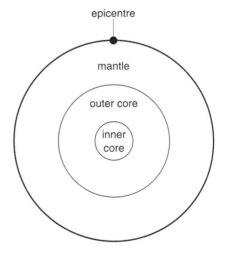

a   Copy the diagram and draw on two typical P waves and two typical S waves.

b   Label a position where a wave is partially reflected.

c   Label a position where a wave is partially refracted.

4.7 The structure of the Earth

Key points

- The Earth consists of a solid inner core, a liquid outer core, the mantle and the crust.
- The outer part of the mantle and the crust together are known as the lithosphere.
- Early last century, the idea of moving continents was proposed.

1 Give the scientific terms that match the following descriptions. (The same term may be used more than once.)

a The major part of the Earth.

b The name of the substance formed when rocks become so hot that they melt.

c Where molten rock comes to the surface.

d The name given to molten rock when it comes to the surface and flows out.

e The name given to the Earth's crust and the outermost part of the mantle.

f The part of the Earth that is about 2800 km thick and contains compounds of magnesium, silicon and iron.

g The process of continents moving apart.

2 The diagram below shows a volcano.

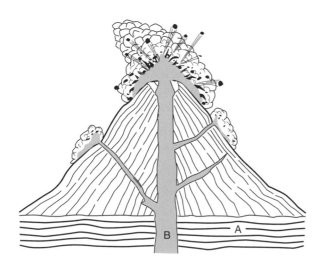

a Copy the diagram and complete the labels.

b What type of rock would be found at A?

c What type of rock would be found at B?

3 The diagram below shows a map of South America placed near a map of Africa, on the same scale.

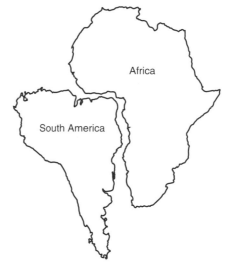

a What is, in fact, between South America and Africa?

b What does the diagram suggest might have happened over a very long period of time?

c What name is given to the process you described in part **b**?

4 In the past it was thought that the Earth was cooling, shrinking and folding. However, the idea of continental drift is now widely accepted. Use the diagram below to help you to answer the questions that follow.

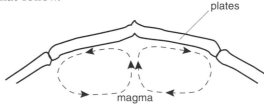

a What is the origin of the heat that heats the magma?

b Describe the process by which the magma moves, as indicated by the arrows on the diagram.

c What is the scientific name for this process of heat transfer?

d How does the movement of the magma explain the movement of the continental plates?

4.8 Plate tectonics

Key points

- The lithosphere is made up of about fifteen tectonic plates which are constantly moving.
- Many earthquake zones are at plate boundaries.

- Where plates collide or separate, geological features such as mountains, island chains and rift valleys are formed.

1 Give the scientific terms that match the following descriptions.

a The theory used to explain the formation of mountains, volcanoes and earthquakes.

b The name given to the fifteen large slabs of rock that compose the lithosphere.

c The layer of flowing mantle that the slabs described in part **b** move on.

d The areas where the oceanic plate descend beneath the continental plate.

e The boundaries between colliding plates.

f The boundaries between separating and splitting plates.

2 The diagram below shows the formation of a rift valley.

a Copy the diagram. Add labels to show the continental crust and the mantle. Add arrows to show directions of movement of the continental crust.

b Explain how these movements cause a rift valley to be formed.

c What may happen if the valley is flooded?

d Give an example of a flooded rift valley.

3 The diagram below shows the formation of a mountain range.

mountain range

a Copy the diagram. Add labels to show the continental crust and the mantle. Add arrows to show directions of movement of the continental crust and mantle.

b Explain how these movements cause a mountain range to be formed.

c Give an example of a mountain range formed in this way.

IDEAS AND EVIDENCE

4 The Himalayas is a young mountain range, in geological terms.

The country of Nepal is a Himalayan Kingdom. It contains eight of the ten highest mountains in the world. It is also one of the poorest countries in the world. The Himalayas are snow-capped all year round and there are many fast flowing rivers. Travel is difficult as there are few roads; most travel is by foot or donkey. To grow crops, small fields must be created on the mountainsides by terracing.

a What advantages do you think Nepal has as a country looking to improve its economy?

b What do you think are the main disadvantages that the people of Nepal face as they seek to develop the country?

The drawing below shows a typical Nepalese 'road' between two villages. There has been a recent landslide.

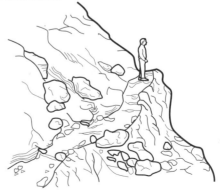

c Why do you think landslides are very common in Nepal?

5.1 What is radioactivity?

Key points

- Radioactivity is radiated from the central nucleus of an atom when the nucleus is unstable.
- The collective name for the protons and neutrons in the nucleus is nucleons.
- There are three main types of ionising radiation: alpha (α) particles, beta (β) particles and gamma (γ) rays.
- Background radiation is all around us.

1

a Name the three main types of ionising radiation.

b Copy and complete the table below to produce a summary of information about the three main types of ionising radiation.

name	description	charge

2

a What is meant by the term 'isotope'?

b The nucleus of an atom is represented in this way

$$^A_Z X$$

What do the letters A, X and Z represent?

c Copy and complete the table below to show the composition of the nuclei of some nuclides.

nucleus	number of protons	number of neutrons
$^{219}_{86}$Rn		
$^{4}_{2}$He		
$^{238}_{92}$U		
$^{14}_{6}$C		

3 Write down the mass number and the atomic number of each of the following nuclides:

a $^{40}_{19}$K

b $^{17}_{8}$O

c $^{225}_{89}$Ac

4

a State the main causes of background radiation.

b Would you expect the level of background radiation to be the same throughout the UK? Explain your answer.

5 In each case below state the type of radiation that is being described:

a a helium nucleus

b electromagnetic waves

c electron

d speed of just less than 3×10^8 m/s

e speed of 3×10^8 m/s

f speed of 1×10^7 m/s

g weakly ionising

h fairly ionising

i very strongly ionising

j stopped by brown paper

k penetrates brown paper but is stopped by 20 mm of aluminium

l penetrates 20 mm of aluminium but is stopped by thick lead

m not deflected by a magnetic field

n deflected a little by a magnetic field

o deflected greatly by a magnetic field

p used in the treatment of deep-seated cancers

q used in thickness gauges measuring the diameters of wires

r used in smoke alarms.

6 Complete the following equations:

a $^{14}_{6}$C $\rightarrow$ $^{14}_{7}$N + ???

b $^{229}_{90}$Th $\rightarrow$ $^{???}_{???}$Ra + $^{4}_{2}$He

c $^{209}_{82}$Pb $\rightarrow$ $^{???}_{83}$Bi + ???

7 Would you expect airline pilots to be exposed to more ionising radiation than airline ground staff? Explain your answer.

5.2 Properties of radiations

Key points

- Radiation causes ionisation in material it passes through by removing electrons from atoms.
- Alpha, beta and gamma radiation travel at different speeds.
- They travel different distances in air.
- They have different penetrative properties.
- These properties mean alpha, beta and gamma radiations can be detected by Geiger–Müller tubes, spark counters and photographic film.

1 Copy and complete the table below about alpha, beta and gamma radiation.

type of radiation	alpha	beta	gamma
charge			
penetrating power			
ionising power			

(Note that for penetrating power and ionising power, numerical values are not required. A description is required, for example 'low', 'very high'.)

2 The diagram shows a Geiger–Müller tube and counter used in an experiment to study a radioactive source.

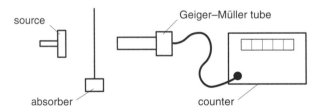

Before the main experiment was started, the Geiger–Müller tube was switched on for 30 minutes. During this time the radioactive source was kept well away from the counter.

a Why do you think the experimenter did this and why was it important?

The main experiment involved recording the count rate from the radioactive source with different absorbers between the source and the Geiger–Müller tube (as shown in the diagram). The table below shows the readings.

absorber	count rate in counts/minute (corrected for background radiation)
none	853
brown paper	632
6 mm aluminium foil	289

b Calculate the contributions (in counts/minute) made to the total activity of the source by alpha, beta and gamma radiation.

c Why was it important to keep the distances between the source, absorber and Geiger–Müller tube constant throughout the experiment?

d The count rates given in the table were 'corrected for background radiation'. Describe how the experimenter would have done this.

3 The diagram below shows a thin wire a few millimetres below a metal grid. The grid is earthed and there is a voltage of a few thousand volts between the wire and the grid. This is used in a school laboratory to demonstrate the principle of the spark counter.

The voltage between the grid and the wire is almost enough to produce a spark in dry air.

a Explain why, when an alpha particle source is held just above the wire, sparks can be seen between the grid and the wire.

b Would you expect to see sparks at regular time intervals while the alpha particle source was in place? Explain your answer.

c A beta particle source does not produce the sparking effect. Explain why.

d Would you expect a gamma ray source to produce sparks? Explain your answer.

4 The process of ionisation is important to the understanding of radioactivity. Explain carefully what is meant by alpha radiation causing ionisation as it passes through a material. Include a diagram to indicate what is happening to the atoms of the material as it is ionised.

5.3 Radioactive decay

Key points

- When a radioisotope emits radiation and changes into another isotope this is known as radioactive decay.
- Radioactive decay is random.
- The activity of an isotope is a measure of its rate of decay.

- The time it takes for radioisotopes to decay varies from isotope to isotope – even isotopes of the same element.
- We measure the radioactive decay time in a 'period' called half-life.
- Different half-lives allow us to use isotopes for particular jobs.

1 What is meant by the term 'half-life'?

2 Some students carried out a random decay simulation experiment. They used 200 small wooden bricks, each of which had a coloured dot on one side only. The bricks were dropped into a tray.

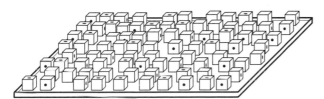

All those that fell coloured dot side uppermost were removed. The number remaining was noted. These were then picked up and dropped into the tray. Again, all those that fell coloured dot side uppermost were removed and the number remaining was noted. The process was repeated until very few remained in the tray. The results are shown in the table below.

throw	number of bricks remaining
0	200
1	175
2	146
3	120
4	96
5	83
6	68
7	57
8	48
9	38
10	33
11	30

a This experiment is a simulation of radioactive decay. What does the 'number of bricks remaining' represent?

b Plot a graph of number of bricks remaining (*y* axis) against throw (*x* axis).

c From your graph find the 'half-life' of the bricks.

d How do you think the number of bricks in the simulation (200) compares with the number of nuclei in a 0.1 g sample of a radioactive isotope?

3

a The half-life of a radioactive isotope is 8 hours. If you have a sample of mass 0.64 g, how long will it take to decay so that 0.08 g of the original isotope remains?

b 10 g of a radioactive isotope decays until only 1.25 g remains. This process takes 4000 years. What is the half-life of the isotope?

4 A radioactive source used in the school laboratory to demonstrate the penetrative power of a beta emitter has a half-life of about 40 years.

a Is a source of this half-life a sensible choice for the school? Explain your answer.

b The activity of this source was recorded every 5 minutes for half an hour. The readings were:

2345 counts/min
2357 counts/min
2363 counts/min
2339 counts/min
2348 counts/min
2360 counts/min

What can you conclude from these readings?

5.4 Using penetrative power of radioactivity

Key points

- Radioactivity has a large number of uses which rely on the differing penetrative power of radiation.

- These uses include thickness measurement, smoke alarms, treatment of cancer and tracer techniques.
- The isotope used is chosen because of both its penetrative properties and its half-life.

1 A smoke detector is set off when smoke prevents the radiation from a source within the detector from reaching a radiation detector.

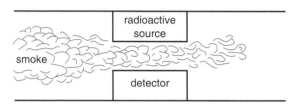

a State the type of source (alpha, beta or gamma) that is suitable for a smoke detector.

b Explain the reasons for your answer in part **a**.

c Suggest a suitable distance between the source and the detector.

d Give a reason for your answer in part **c**.

2 The diagram below shows a thickness gauge used to monitor the thickness of aluminium foil.

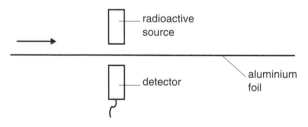

a State the type of source (alpha, beta or gamma) that is suitable for a thickness gauge.

b Explain the reasons for your answer in part **a**.

c What are the advantages of using this type of thickness gauge rather than a very accurate measuring instrument such as a micrometer screw gauge?

3 Radioactive sources can be used as tracers. The diagram below shows an example. The source is used to find a leak in an underground oil pipeline.

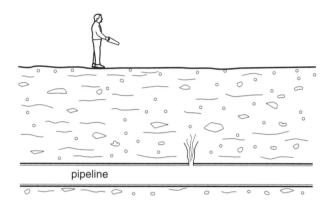

a State the type of source (alpha, beta or gamma) that is suitable for a leak detector.

b Explain the reasons for your answer in part **a**.

c Describe briefly an alternative method of finding the leak. What are the advantages of using a radioactive tracer?

4 The diagram below shows a radioactive source being used to treat a deep-seated cancer.

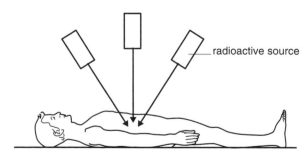

a State the type of source (alpha, beta or gamma) that is suitable for this treatment.

b Explain the reasons for your answer in part **a**.

c Why is the radiation made to enter the body in a number of different and very carefully controlled directions?

5.5 Other uses of radioactivity

Key points

- Radioactivity has a large number of other uses including sterilisation and dating of artefacts and rocks.

1 The activity due to carbon-14 in a sample of 1.0 g of living wood is 16.0 counts/minute. The remains of an ancient wooden ship have been found.

Archaeologists have found that the level of radioactivity in a 1.0 g sample of wood from the ship is 4 counts/minute. The half-life of carbon-14 is 5568 years.

a How old is the ship?

b Assuming that the measurements were carried out with great care, how accurate do you think this value is likely to be?

c Give a reason for your answer to part **b**.

2 The radioactive isotope of carbon is often called 'carbon-14'.

a What does '14' mean in this context?

b Write down a representation of the nucleus of carbon-14 in symbolic form.

c Carbon-14 has a very long half-life (about 5500 years). What is meant by the term 'half-life'.

The amount of carbon-14 in some types of materials allows radioactive dating to be carried out.

d What type of materials can be used?

e Explain your answer to part **d**.

3 Two neighbours have been in dispute over a tree that is on a common boundary between their gardens.

The tree has recently died and the police suspect that one of the neighbours may have poisoned it. As part of their enquiries they need to establish when it died.

a Would carbon-14 dating be a suitable method for establishing the date of the tree's death?

b Explain your answer to part **a**.

4 Some archaeologists want to find the age of some fragments of ancient cloth. The fragments are thought to be about 2000 years old.

a Do you think that carbon-14 dating would be a suitable dating method?

b How accurate do you think carbon-14 dating would be?

c What assumptions are made in order to use carbon-14 dating?

5 Sterilisation is an important technique used to destroy bacteria.

a What type of radiation is used in sterilisation?

b Suggest why this type of radiation is the most suitable and why the other types are unsuitable.

c List at least four types of items that are sterilised in this way.

6 The diagram below shows how a radioactive source is used to monitor the packaging of tablets. The amount of radiation penetrating a particular section of the packet is less than expected if there is no tablet in place. In this case the packet is automatically rejected.

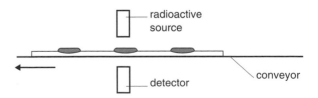

a What type of radioactive source (alpha, beta or gamma) would be most suitable?

b Explain your answer to part **a**.

c Would you be concerned about the tablets becoming contaminated with radioactivity?

d Explain your answer to part **c**.

5.6 Using radioactivity safely

Key points

- Exposure to radioactivity is dangerous.
- Radiation effects are cumulative.
- Radiation can cause burns, sickness, reduction in lymphocyte count, hair loss, as well as cancer.

- People who use radioactivity need to observe safety precautions based on the properties of the radiations.

1 The diagrams below show a radioactive source used in a school laboratory. Comment on the safety precautions that are taken. Refer to each diagram in turn, indicating how safety is being maintained and the reasons for the precautions.

a

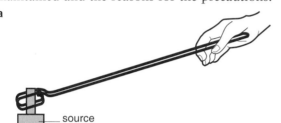
source

b

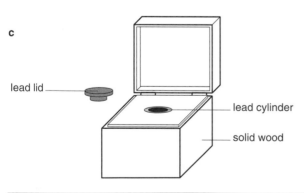

c

lead lid
lead cylinder
solid wood

2 The diagram below shows the experimental arrangement used to test the penetrative power of alpha, beta and gamma radiation.

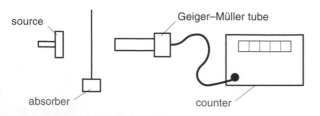
source
Geiger–Müller tube
absorber
counter

a Explain what is meant by 'penetrative power'.

After the final experiment the teacher very carefully picks up the source with long-handled tongs and places it in its container. However, after that, she picks up the absorber with her fingers.

b Was picking up the absorber with her fingers a dangerous thing to do?

c Explain your answer to part **b**.

3 A technician is testing a container that is being used to store radioactive waste materials.

a What is the badge that the technician is wearing?

b Explain how the badge works.

c Explain the importance of the badge to the technician.

Radioactive waste like this may have a half-life of many hundreds of years. It could be buried deep underground or put into steel and concrete containers and dropped to the bottom of the sea.

d State and explain your views on this type of disposal of radioactive waste.

IDEAS AND EVIDENCE

4 It has been suggested that radioactive waste with very long half-lives could be sent into space, millions of miles away from the Earth.

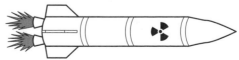

Give your own views on the possible advantages and disadvantages of this method of disposal of radioactive waste materials.

6.1 **Our Solar System**

> ## Key points
>
> - Our Solar System is just one of many star systems in our galaxy.
> - Our galaxy is just one of many in the Universe.
> - Planets orbit stars and moons orbit planets.
> - There are many other types of body in space.
> - Some bodies are natural and some are man made.
> - These man-made artificial satellites have many uses.

1

a What are planets?
b What is a meteor?
c What are asteroids?
d What is a comet?
e What is a natural satellite?
f What is an artificial satellite?

2

a List the planets in order, starting from the Sun.
b Which planets are rocky?
c What are the others made of?
d Write down one other fact about each planet.

3 Explain why the Earth stays in orbit round the Sun and the Moon stays in orbit round the Earth. Hint: You must mention what gravity is, why it occurs and how far it extends.

4 Table A contains information about three artificial satellites orbiting the Earth.

Table A

satellite	altitude in km	period in hours
TRMM	350	
NOAA N		1.70
Jason-1	1336	

Table B relates the altitude of a satellite to its period. Plot a graph of the data given in table B. Use your graph to complete table A.

Table B

altitude in km	period in hours
0	1.41
400	1.55
800	1.69
1200	1.83
1600	1.98
2000	2.13

What can you say about the relationship between the altitude of a satellite and its period?

5 Use these three pieces of information about comets to explain how they move through the Solar System.

- The speed of comets can vary from 200 km per hour to 20 million km per hour, depending upon their distance from the Sun.
- Halley's comet was last seen from the Earth in 1986. Some of you may see it again in 2061.
- Kepler stated that the paths of planets sweep out equal areas from the Sun in equal times.

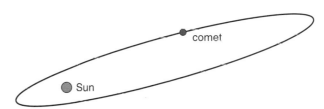

6

a What are stars and galaxies?
b Draw a sketch of our galaxy and mark the position of our 'local star'.
c Describe what it looks like to look along the galaxy and to look out of our galaxy.

a Using the data in question **4** and knowing that the radius of the Earth is 6370 km, work out the speeds of the satellites.
b How does the speed change with the height? Why is this?
c By carefully extrapolating the graph you have drawn in question **4**, estimate the altitude of a geostationary satellite.

Hint: A geostationary satellite has a period of 24 hours.

6.2 The life cycle of stars (1)

Key points

- Stars form within clouds of dust and gas in space.
- Gravitational forces cause part of a dust cloud to contract.
- The contraction causes heating.
- A star is formed when the temperature is great enough for hydrogen nuclei to fuse into helium nuclei releasing energy.
- As the fusion of hydrogen nuclei into helium nuclei in the star's core comes to an end, the star expands into a red giant.
- A small star, like our Sun, contracts and becomes a white dwarf, which changes colour and fades as it cools.
- Massive starts glow brightly again as they continue to fuse.

- Massive stars expand and contract several times and form the nuclei of heavier elements before becoming a supernova.
- An expanding supernova throws layers of dust and gas into space, leaving behind a very dense core called a neutron star.
- Second generation stars, such as our Sun, can form in the clouds of dust and gas from the exploding supernova.
- Sometimes the core of a supernova contains too much material and goes on collapsing, forming a black hole.
- A black hole has such a large gravitational force that not even light can escape from it.

1 Explain these terms, related to the life cycle of stars:

a protostar

b main sequence star

c red giant

d white dwarf

e supernova

f neutron star

g black hole.

2 Construct a flow chart to show how the stages listed in question **1** fit together in the life cycles of stars.

3 Second generation stars, such as our Sun, can form in the dust from a supernova explosion. These glowing clouds of gas and dust are called supernova remnants. Gravitational forces cause part of a dust cloud to contract.

Explain what is meant by:

a second generation

b supernova remnants

c form in the dust

d gravitational forces.

4 The diagram below is a special diagram that shows the positions of different types of stars according to their apparent brightness and their temperature. Hot bright stars are in the top left, cool faint stars are in the bottom right and so on. The stars across the middle are 'main sequence' stars. They have a complete range of temperatures and brightnesses. Our Sun is just below the middle of the main sequence band of stars.

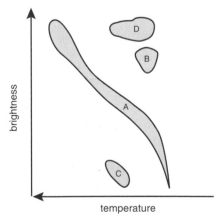

Copy the diagram and put in the names of the types of stars at positions A to D.

5 Stars in the main sequence are stable. Massive convection currents carry energy from the nuclear reactions at the centre to the surface. These outward forces are balanced by the star's gravity. Explain what happens to the star when the supply of hydrogen runs out.

Continued ▶

6.2 The life cycle of stars (2)

6 Explain why we say that a black hole is 'black'.

7 Our Sun started out as interstellar dust from a supernova explosion. After moving through the main sequence and red giant stages, it will become a very hot bright star before finishing its existence as a black dwarf.

a Copy the diagram from question **4**. Draw a dotted line on the star diagram to show the path of the life of our Sun.

b Draw a continuous line on your diagram to show the path of a massive star. This starts as interstellar gas but becomes a very hot main sequence star and ends its existence in a supernova explosion.

8 The nuclear reactions taking place in the Sun are quite complex. This is one possible reaction.

$^{1}_{1}H + ^{2}_{1}H \rightarrow ^{3}_{2}He + energy$

Use the atomic masses below to work out the amount of matter converted into energy, in joules, each time one helium atom is formed.

$^{1}_{1}H = 1.0076$ amu

$^{2}_{1}H = 2.0142$ amu

$^{3}_{2}He = 3.0021$ amu

1 amu is approx. 2×10^{-27} kg

(Hint: Use the Einstein equation, $E = mc^2$)

9

a Explain why the mass and brightness of a main sequence star are related.

The relationship is brightness α mass^3

Hint: These stars are mainly hydrogen.

b The brightness varies from 1×10^{-4} Suns to 1×10^6 Suns. By what factor do the masses change?

10 The Sun loses energy at the rate of 4.0×10^{26} J/s and loses mass at a rate of 4.4×10^9 kg/s. Is this consistent with the Einstein equation for the conversion of matter into energy? (See question 8.)

6.3 The evolution of the Universe (1)

Key points

- The whole Universe is expanding.
- It might have started billions of years ago in one place with a huge explosion – the Big Bang.
- Theories for the origin of the Universe take into account that light from other galaxies is shifted to the red end of the spectrum and the further away the galaxies are, the greater the red shift.
- One way of explaining this is that other galaxies are moving away from us very quickly and galaxies furthest from us are moving fastest.
- There are possible futures for the Universe depending on the amount of mass in the Universe and the speed at which the galaxies are moving apart.
- Knowledge of the rate of expansion of the Universe enables its age to be estimated.
- Scientists are trying to find evidence for life on other planets in the Solar System and elsewhere in the Universe.

1

a Put the following in order of increasing size:

- asteroid
- galaxy
- meteor
- moon
- planet
- red giant
- the Sun
- Universe
- white dwarf.

b Which of the above do not produce light of their own?

2 Draw a series of circles with radii 5, 4, 3, 2 and 1 cm, starting with the largest. Each time you draw a circle move the compass point 0.5 cm forward. This should give you a nest of circles that are closer together on one side than the other. They represent circular sound waves produced by a moving source, at a scale of 1 cm = 1 m.

a What is the wavelength of the sound:

i ahead of the source?
ii behind the source?

b What would have been the wavelength of the sound if the source had not been moving?

c If sound travels at 300 m/s what is the frequency of the sound heard:

i ahead of the source?
ii behind the source?
iii if the source is not moving?

d Explain what would you hear as the source of sound passed you?

3 Explain what the red shift is and how it enables scientists to estimate the speed of recession of galaxies.

4 Explain how the knowledge of the speed and separation of galaxies in the Universe could be used to support the idea of a Big Bang creation theory of the Universe and how scientists can tell how long ago the Big Bang occurred.

5 Our galaxy was once thought to be the limit of the Universe. Now we believe that there are may millions of such galaxies.

a What evidence is there that there is life in other parts of the Universe?

b Would it be possible to find and communicate with life elsewhere?

6 The mass-density of the Universe will determine whether it will continue to expand for ever or eventually contract again.

- For a mass-density less than 1 it will continue to expand.
- For a mass-density greater than 1 gravity will be strong enough to make the Universe contract.

It is thought that the value is less than 1. Explain what you think might happen to the Universe.

Continued ▶

6.3 The evolution of the Universe (2)

7 According to the Hubble law, the speed at which galaxies are moving apart is proportional to their separation. The graph below shows a possible relationship between the speed and separation of the galaxies in the Universe.

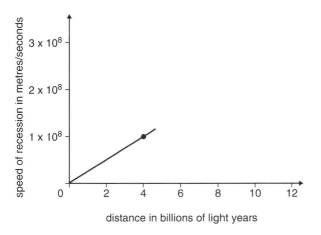

a Extrapolate the graph to estimate the distance of separation when the speed of recession is equal to the speed of light.

b The most distant objects that we can see are quasars. It is estimated that they are about twelve thousand million light years away. They show a significant red shift, suggesting that they are travelling at nearly the speed of light. Discuss whether this information puts a limit on the size of the Universe. If so what would that limit be?

8 Cepheid variables are stars that change in brightness. Some of them are too faint to be seen from Earth. The Hubble Space Telescope, which orbits the Earth at 575 km, way above the atmosphere, has found them in galaxies in most parts of the Universe. They become very bright and then gradually fade. The time taken for one cycle tells us how bright the star is. (Can you think why?) If we then compare its brightness in the sky with its real brightness we can tell us how far away it is.

a What are the variable stars called?

b What is their special behaviour?

c What does it tell us about the star?

d How do they help in measuring how far galaxies are away?

e Why is the Hubble Space Telescope important in this work?

IDEAS AND EVIDENCE

9 About 70 years ago Karl Jansky published the account of how he first received radio waves from space. Since then radio astronomy has been providing valuable information about our Sun and about stars right out to the edge of the observable universe. Even on cloudy nights, when optical telescopes are of no use, the radio sky seems uniformly bright. However, we can access only a small proportion of the information carried by radio waves, as most are reflected back by the Earth's ionosphere.

Fortunately though there is a radio window that lets through radio waves of wavelengths between 2 cm and 100 m and two important wavelengths of radio waves from excited hydrogen atoms come in this region.

Some of the brightest radio sources are from optically dark parts of galaxies, places where the hydrogen gas clouds that surround galaxies are colliding at enormously high speeds. The Crab Nebula is a bright radio emitter and is thought to be the remnant of a supernova observed in the same place and recorded by Chinese observers in 1054.

Explain what is meant by:

a radio astronomy

b uniformly bright

c reflected back

d the ionosphere

e radio window

f optically dark

g colliding at enormously high speeds.

h what important contributions to our understanding of the Universe have been made by radio astronomy?

7.1 Electrostatic phenomena

Key points

- Electrical insulators can become charged by friction or by direct contact. Charging involves the movement of electrons.

- Law of electric charge – like charges repel, unlike charges attract.
- Objects can also become charged by induction.

1 Explain the following terms. Write down a practical example of each to illustrate your answer.

a conductor
b insulator
c current
d voltage
e negative charge
f cell
g electrical earth.

2

a Explain how the charges move when you rub a plastic rod with a clean dry duster:

  i when the rod charges negatively
  ii when the rod charges positively.

b Why does the rod have to be dry and the duster clean?

3

a Write down the law of charge.

b You have a balloon that is charged positively. You test the following objects with the balloon. List the results, using these terms: 'repels', 'attracts', 'has no effect'.

  i positive balloon
  ii negative balloon
  iii uncharged paper pieces
  iv charged Perspex (positive)
  v steam from a kettle
  vi uncharged pieces of aluminium foil.

4 Explain what is happening in these common situations. Mention 'charges' in your answer. You can assume that all these things charge positively.

a You tear open the plastic envelope round your favourite magazine and a small piece of plastic comes off and sticks to your hand. It won't drop into the bin and it won't shake off either.

b You are dusting the top of the hi-fi because it is covered in dust. As you dust it, even more dust sticks to the surface.

c You slide off the plastic upholstery of a car seat and get a sharp shock as you go the close the car door.

5 You have a tin can and a plastic rod which charges positively. The can stands on an uncharged insulator. Draw a series of diagrams showing how you would charge the can

a by contact
b by induction.

  Show, on your diagrams what happens to the charges.

c In one of the methods, the can has the same charge as the rod; in the other, it has the opposite. Which is which?

6 Explain what is happening in this series of experiments. The leaf of the electroscope rises when the apparatus is charged. It will fall when the apparatus is discharged or an equal and opposite charge is brought nearby.

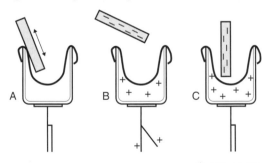

7 Copy these pictures below and add charges to show how they are distributed. In some pictures you will have to use both positive and negative charges.

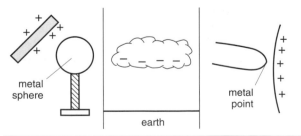

8 The capacitance of a small metal ball is proportional to its radius. The Earth has a capacitance proportional to its radius. Explain why a small charged ball is completely discharged (that is, loses all its charge) when it is connected to 'earth'.

7.2 Uses and problems of electrostatics

Key points

- Electrostatics can be put to good use in a variety of ways.

- Some problems caused by static electricity include the risk of explosion when re-fuelling aircraft.

1 Make a list of six situations where you meet static charges in your daily life. Explain what you think is happening in each case and say whether the situation is useful or a nuisance.

2 As petrol is a non-conducting liquid, it can charge up as it flows through pipes made of materials that are insulators. Explain what is happening in the following situations:

a an aeroplane and a airport petrol tanker are always connected together with a thick copper cable before refuelling starts

b petrol hoses at petrol stations have a metal strip down the inside of the hose which is connected to earth at one end and the metal nozzle at the other. The nozzle should be resting on the metal of the car before refuelling starts.

3 Explain how electrostatic charges are used in the production of photocopies or laser copies.

4 Electrostatic precipitators are very efficient in the removal of dust from smoky chimneys. Draw the following diagram and explain how the precipitator works.

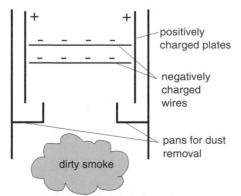

5 Electrostatic charges are useful in two separate ways when spraying liquids. Firstly the particles in the spray are charged and spread out, and secondly, they are attracted to earthed or oppositely charged surfaces. Draw diagrams and use them to help you explain:

a why the particles spread out

b why the particles are attracted to the surface that is being sprayed.

6

a Explain why the tubes that carry flour in a bakery are lined with a conducting material and are connected to earth.

b Explain why careful earthing is required when replacing computer chips, especially those using CMOS technology.

7 Electrostatic paint spraying is very effective when shaped objects are being sprayed. Even the reverse side of metal plates can be sprayed. Explain how this is achieved.

8 Plants that grow in soil are generally at earth potential. Explain how this useful when spraying crops with solutions of fertilisers or insecticides. Why do you think the technique is particularly useful when spraying trees. Illustrate you answer with a diagram.

9 Electrostatic spraying is so effective that smaller drops can be used and less liquid is required. Explain, referring to painting and crop spraying, how you think that electrostatic spraying is beneficial in keeping costs low, the effectiveness of the spray and the effect on pollution.

10 Helicopters generate a considerable amount of static electricity during flight.

a Explain how you think that this occurs.

b What do you think must be done when the helicopter lands?

7.3 Charge and current

Key points

- Electric current is a flow of charge.
- Current in a metal is due to electrons.
- Current in an electrolytic solution is due to ions.

H Charge and current are linked by the equation charge = current × time

H Voltage is the energy transferred by unit charge. 1 volt = 1 joule/coulomb

1 When charges move a current flows. Explain what moves in each of these substances to allow a current to flow. Illustrate your answer with a practical example of each:

a a gas   b a salt solution   c a metal.

2 There are a number of experiments where static electricity is converted into current electricity. Here is one of them. Copy the diagram of the apparatus and explain what is happening.

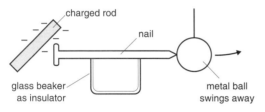
charged rod
nail
glass beaker as insulator
metal ball swings away

3 Learn the equation $Q = It$

Q is in coulombs, I is in amps and t is in seconds.

Use the equation to calculate:

a how much charge flows round a circuit, if 3 A flows for 88 s

b the current, if 120 C of charge moves round the circuit in 80 s

c how long it takes to charge a capacitor with 0.5 C if the average current is 0.1 A.

4 Learn the equation $V = W/Q$

V is in volts, W is in joules and Q is in coulombs.

Use the equation to calculate:

a the work done when 10 C of charge flows out of a 12 V battery

b the voltage of a dynamo, if 560 J of work is done producing 80 C of charge

c the charge (in mC) on a capacitor if 0.3 J of work is done charging it to a voltage of 100 V.

d the work done moving an electron through a potential of 1 V (this amount of energy is called an electronvolt. $e = 1.6 \times 10^{-19}$ C).

5 For each of the following situations, draw two diagrams: **i** when there is no voltage and **ii** with a voltage, positive on the left.

a a section of wire showing metal nuclei and free electrons

b a beaker of copper sulphate solution with two copper electrodes showing Cu^{2+} and SO_4^{2-} ions

c a fluorescent tube showing electrons and gas ions in a vacuum between two electrodes.

6 Inside a thunder cloud, charged ice crystals and ionised air particles, in huge convection currents, leave positive charges at the top of the cloud and negative charges at the bottom.

a When a lightning flash occurs, negative charge travels through the air to earth. Use the equations

$$Q = It \text{ and } V = W/Q$$

to calculate the energy in one flash.

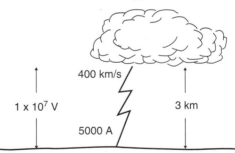
400 km/s
1×10^7 V
3 km
5000 A

(Hint: Find the time taken for the flash. Then, knowing the current, calculate the charge. Then you can calculate the work done.)

b What would be the speed of a 20 000 kg lorry that had this amount of kinetic energy?

7 The current in a TV tube is 13 mA.

a How many electrons hit the screen per second?

Each electron is accelerated through a voltage of 0.6 kV.

b What is the kinetic energy of one electron?

c What is the total energy converted into heat on the screen?

7.4 Electricity in the home

Key points

- Electrical power = voltage × current
- In direct current the electrons always move in one direction but in alternating current the electrons oscillate (move to and fro).

- Electricity is supplied to your house using a cable with three wires – live, neutral and earth.

1 Use the equation $V = IR$ to calculate:

a the current in a circuit where a 6 V battery is connected to a 12 Ω resistor

b the voltage across a 15 Ω resistor which carries a current of 2.5 A

c the resistance of a lead when the current through it is 2 A and the voltage across it is 0.5 V.

2 These electrical items may work on a battery, the mains or both. Construct a table with the headings 'mains', 'battery', 'both' and put the items in the correct columns.

- calculator
- DVD player
- electric screwdriver
- iron
- kettle
- mobile phone
- oven
- personal stereo
- toaster
- torch
- TV
- vacuum cleaner.

3 Explain the differences between a.c. and d.c. used in the home in terms of:

a the movement of electrons in a wire

b how the electrical energy is produced

c how convenient it is to use

d how much electrical energy can be obtained.

4 Copy the table below and fill in the gaps using the power formula.

	voltage, V, in V	current, I, in A	power, in W
kettle	230		2200
car starter motor		100	1200
hairdryer	230	7.0	
torch bulb	3.5	0.3	
curling tongs	230		400
screwdriver		2.0	4.8

5 Copy and complete the table below.

colour of wire	name of wire	purpose of wire
	live	
	neutral	
	earth	

6

a Draw a simplified version of a ring main circuit. Show the consumer unit with the fuse and show how the sockets are connected to the three wires of the ring.

b Explain how the electric current to a particular appliance flows from the supply to the socket.

7

a Use the equation $V = W/Q$ to explain why an electric screwdriver that works off a 2.4 V battery is less powerful than one that works off a 7.2 V battery.

b Explain what happens when each screwdriver is made to do more work when it is slowed down by a tight screw.

8 Copy the sine waves below that represent the a.c. current and voltage in a resistor. By measuring various heights along the graph, draw a curve that represents the power dissipated.

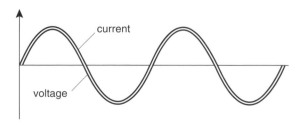

Hint: Measure the values at the peaks and near the peaks. The current and voltage are sometimes both negative and sometimes both zero.

7.5 Electrical safety

Key points

- Fuses and circuit breakers are used to prevent fire due to electrical faults. Fuses melt if the current becomes too large.
- The earth wire helps to prevent electric shock by providing a low resistance path between the case of an appliance and the earth.
- Double-insulated appliances are not earthed; there are no electrical connections to the outer case.

1 Explain the reason for these following electrical safety features. Draw a sketch or a circuit diagram if you think it will improve your answer.

a The switch for a light fitting is in the live wire.

b Electrical wires are covered with plastic.

c A bathroom light has a switch operated by a cord pull.

d The terminals of a plug are coated with plastic around the top.

e Kettles have thick wires, TVs have thin wires.

f Electric hedge cutters are RCD protected.

g Appliances have their power printed on them.

h In the consumer unit, 5 A fuse holders fit into small sockets whereas 30 A fuse holders fit into large sockets.

2 Explain this statement about electrical safety: 'fuses and circuit breakers prevent fires due to electrical faults'.

a State what would happen in the event of a fault if there was no fuse or circuit breaker.

b Explain how the fuse or circuit breaker helps to prevent damage.

3 Use the equation $P = V \times I$ to calculate the maximum current through the following electrical appliances. In the right-hand column, write the appropriate fuse size. Possible sizes are 3 A, 5 A and 13 A. Use voltage = 230 V.

appliance	power in W	maximum current in A	suitable fuse size in A
table lamp	60		
colour TV	300		
iron	1600		
hairdryer	1400		
fan heater	2400		

4 Copy the lighting diagram below and put in:

a L and N for the live and neutral

b switches for the two bedroom lights

c one switch to control both landing lights

d the fuse for the circuit.

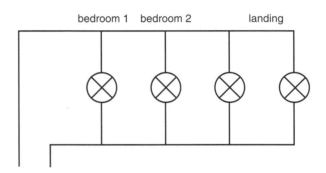

bedroom 1   bedroom 2   landing

5 Draw a labelled diagram of a 13 A plug.

6 Explain this statement about electrical safety: 'the earth wire together with the fuse or circuit breaker, prevents electrocution'.

Hint: Be careful to explain the role of the earth wire before and after the fuse blows.

7 Double-insulated appliances do not need an earth wire. What sort of appliances are double-insulated and what does it mean?

8

a Explain how a fuse works.

b Explain how a circuit breaker works.

c Write down some of the advantages and disadvantages of circuit breakers compared with fuses.

9 Use the equation $P = V \times I$ to calculate the maximum power that can be supplied from a 230 V supply through:

a a 3 A fuse   b a 5 A fuse   c a 13 A fuse.

7.6 Paying for electricity

Key points

- The energy transferred (power × time) can be calculated in joules (W × s) and in kilowatt-hours (kW × h).

- The kilowatt-hour is the commercial unit of electricity so the cost of using various domestic electrical appliances can be found.

1

a The cost of using an electrical appliance depends on its power. Put the following appliances in a rough order of how much power they use, starting with the lowest:

- cooker
- electric drill
- electric fire
- hairdryer
- iron
- kettle
- Christmas tree light bulb
- portable radio cassette player.
- bedside lamp light bulb
- food processor
- fridge freezer
- portable fan
- transistor radio
- vacuum cleaner

b These appliances produce heat, light, sound, motion or a mixture of these types of energy. Put the types of energy into a rough order of increasing energy. Which types of appliance are the most expensive to use and which type are the least expensive?

2 Energy can be transferred from the electricity supply as convection currents by using a convector heater. Electrical energy can also be converted into waves in the electromagnetic spectrum, for example ultraviolet waves, light waves, infrared waves, microwaves and radio waves.

Give a household example of each and explain how expensive they are to produce compared with a 2 kW convector heater.

3 Use the equation energy = power × time to calculate the energy, in joules, that is needed to:

a use a 2.2 kW kettle for 2 minutes

Hint: 2.2 kW = 2200 W, 2 min = 120 s.

b use a 300 W food processor for 5 minutes

c leave a 60 W light bulb on for 2 hours

d listen to a 20 W radio for an hour.

e Calculate the cost of running these appliances if the cost of a unit is 8p.

4 The joule and the kilowatt-hour are both units of energy used to measure electrical energy.

a Calculate the number of joules in one kilowatt-hour. A kilowatt-hour is called one 'unit'.

b How much electrical energy is transferred into heat when a 3 kW fire is on for 4 hours? Give you answer in kilowatt-hours and in joules.

c Why is the kilowatt-hour used instead of the joule when calculating how much energy we use at home?

d What measures the amount of energy used?

5 Compare the cost and convenience of running a transistor radio on batteries and on the mains. Support your answer with calculations. The radio operates using four D-type cells which cost £1.80 per pair and, when on quietly, takes 20 mA. The cells are rated at 2.2 amphour. Operated on the mains, the internal transformer takes 25 mA from the 230 V supply. The unit cost of electricity is 8p.

Hint: Calculate the time the batteries will last (2.2 A/20 mA in hours) and work out the cost of the energy taken from the mains in that time.

6

a A solar cell costs 50p to make. It has dimensions 5 cm × 2.5 cm. In bright sunlight it will produce 100 mA at 500 mV. When electricity costs 8p per unit, roughly how long would a solar cell have to last to pay for its construction costs?

b If the ambient sunlight on the cell has an intensity of 500 W/m^2, how efficient is the cell in converting light into electricity?

7 In one town, electricity is supplied at a cost of 5.02p per unit and gas at 1.327p per unit. Does this mean that electrical heating is more expensive than gas heating?

8.1 Force on a wire in a magnetic field

Key points

- If a wire carrying a current is placed at right angles to a magnetic field there is a force on the wire that may make it move.
- A bigger current or a bigger magnetic field will increase the size of the force on the wire.

- Reversing the current *or* the magnetic field will reverse the direction of the force. Fleming's left-hand rule tells you the direction of this force.
- A loudspeaker makes use of this effect.

1 The diagram below shows how a student held the thumb and first two fingers of his left hand to use Fleming's left-hand rule.

Describe clearly how you would use this rule to find the direction of movement of a current-carrying wire in a magnetic field.

2 The diagrams below show a number of arrangements used to study the effect of a magnetic field on a current-carrying wire.

In each case, describe clearly in which direction the wire will move (or state that it will not move). Justify your answer in each case.

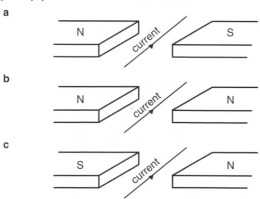

a

b

c

3 The diagram below shows a cross-section of a loudspeaker. The permanent magnet is fixed. The coil is able to move.

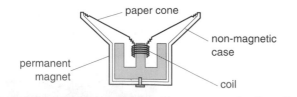

a What is meant by the term 'permanent magnet'?

A student was investigating how a loudspeaker works. She had a non-magnetic case and paper cone as shown in the diagram and was able to fit different permanent magnets and different coils.

She fitted the weakest of the magnets and a coil. She supplied a very small current to the coil. The coil moved a small distance to the right.

b How could the student change the apparatus to make a coil move further? (There is more than one method; give as many as you can.)

c How could the student make the coil move to the left?

d How could the student make the coil oscillate left and right.

e How could the student make the coil oscillate with greater frequency?

4 The diagram below shows a wire connected to a sensitive, centre-zero ammeter. Part of the wire is held between the poles of a magnet.

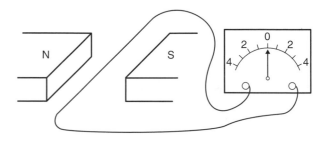

When the wire is moved vertically upwards at a speed of 1 m/s, the ammeter needle moves 2 divisions to the right.

a What will the ammeter show if the wire is moved vertically upwards at a speed of 2 m/s?

b What will the ammeter show if the wire is moved vertically downwards at a speed of 0.5 m/s?

8.2 Electric motors

Key points

- When a coil of wire is placed in a magnetic field, equal and opposite forces act on the sides of it, making it spin.
- A split-ring commutator is needed to produce continuous rotation.

- Motors can be made more powerful by increasing the current in the coil, the number of turns on the coil or the strength of the magnetic field.

1 The diagram below shows a simple electric motor, which works from a d.c. supply.

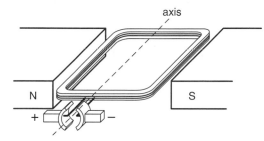

a Explain clearly the purpose of the split-ring commutator.

b Explain clearly how the split-ring commutator works.

c Use Fleming's left-hand rule to predict the direction in which the coil will spin.

2 In a motor, the current passes through 'carbon brushes' to the split-ring commutator.

Give reasons for the use of carbon.

3 The diagram shows a simple electric motor.

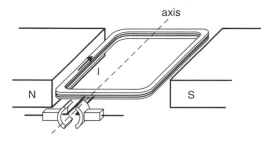

a Copy the diagram and mark on it the forces that make it spin.

b State the rule that you used to predict the direction of spin.

c Explain, in terms of the forces acting on it, why the coil spins (use the words 'moment' or 'couple').

4 The diagram below shows a motor similar to that in question **3**. The motor shown here is more efficient.

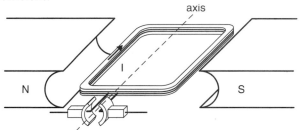

Explain how the change in design makes the motor more efficient. Include a diagram in your answer to show the shape of the magnetic field lines between the two magnetic poles.

5 The electric motor used to power a lift must be very powerful.

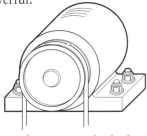

There are several ways in which the power of a motor can be increased. For each of the following examples, explain how the power is increased:

a a change in the number of turns on the coil

b a change in the current supplied to the coil

c a change in the strength of the magnet.

There are some other more complex ways of increasing the power. Explain each one from the list below:

d using an iron core

e using curved pole pieces

f using several coils wound around the same core.

8.3 Electromagnetic induction

Key points

- A voltage is generated when a conductor cuts magnetic field lines. The conductor or the magnet (or both) must move.
- Faraday's Law tells us that the size of the induced voltage depends on the rate of cutting magnetic field lines.

- Lenz's Law tells us that the direction of the induced voltage (or current) always tries to oppose the motion or change producing it. This is the law of conservation of energy.

1 The diagram shows how a student held the thumb and first two fingers of his right hand to use Fleming's right-hand rule.

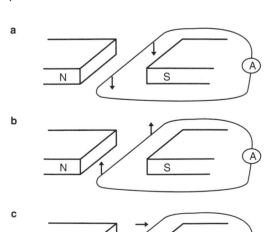

Describe clearly how you would use this rule to find the direction of movement of a current-carrying wire in a magnetic field.

2 The diagrams below show a number of arrangements used to study the current induced in a wire when the wire cuts magnetic field lines. Copy each diagram and, in each case, state the direction of the induced current (if any). Justify your answer in each case.

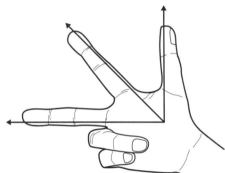

3 The diagram below shows a magnet and a coil. The coil is part of a circuit, including a sensitive centre-zero ammeter.

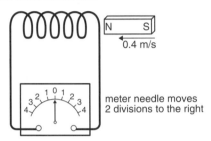

meter needle moves
2 divisions to the right

When the N pole of the magnet is moved into the coil at a speed of 0.4 m/s, the ammeter needle deflects 2 divisions to the right.

In each of the cases shown below, state the magnitude of the ammeter deflection (if any) and its direction.

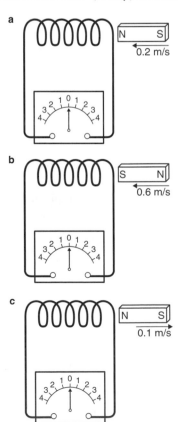

8.4 Generators and mutual induction

> ## Key points
>
> - An alternating current is generated when a coil rotates within a magnetic field or when a magnet rotates within a coil of wire.
>
> - An increase in the rate of rotation leads to a bigger induced current of higher frequency.

1 The diagram below shows a simple a.c. generator.

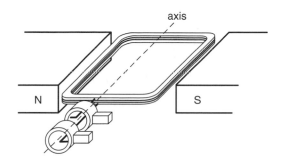

axis

N   S

a Explain the difference between the split-ring commutator, used in a d.c. dynamo, and the slip rings used in the a.c. generator.

The graph below shows the output of an a.c. generator.

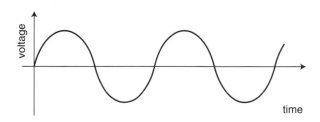

voltage

time

b Copy the graph and label it to show how the output changes as the generator rotates through 360°. Use the diagrams below that show end views of the coil to help you.

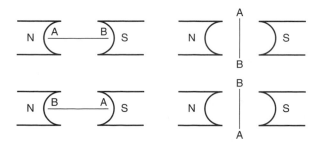

2 The diagram below shows a flow meter, used to monitor the flow of oil in a pipeline.

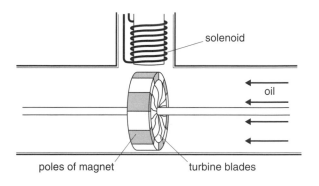

solenoid

oil

poles of magnet   turbine blades

The moving oil causes the turbine blades to rotate, so moving the magnets.

a Explain the effect that the moving magnets have on the solenoid.

b What is the effect of a faster oil flow?

The output of the solenoid is fed to an oscilloscope.

c Draw the type of trace you would expect to see on the oscilloscope. Assume that the time base is set so that the trace includes the passage of three magnets past the solenoid.

3 The diagram shows a model steam engine that is being used to turn a small a.c. generator that can supply a current to light a lamp.

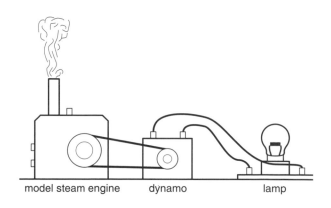

model steam engine   dynamo   lamp

It is noticed that when the lamp circuit is turned on, the steam engine slows down. Explain this in terms of energy.

8.5 Transformers

Key points

- A transformer consists of two coils of wire wound on an iron core. An alternating voltage produces a changing magnetic field in one coil of wire. This induces an alternating voltage in the other coil.

- If the number of turns on the secondary (second) coil is greater than the number on the primary (first) coil, the voltage is increased (and vice versa).
- The transformer allows voltages to be increased (a step-up transformer) or decreased (a step-down transformer).

1 The diagram shows a step-up transformer.

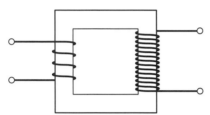

a Copy the diagram and label the following:
- iron core
- primary coil
- secondary coil
- input
- output.

b How did you know which was the primary coil and which was the secondary coil?

2 A transformer consists of a primary coil and a secondary coil, both wound on an iron core. The coils are insulated from each other and from the iron core. Answer the following questions to describe how a transformer works.

a Does an electric current pass from the primary coil to the secondary coil? Explain your answer.

b What effect does the alternating current supplied to the primary coil have in and around the coil?

c What does this produce in the iron core?

d What does the effect produced in the iron core, described in part **c**, produce in the secondary coil?

3 The table below gives some details of transformers. Copy and complete the table; all the transformers are 100% efficient.

V_p in V	N_p	V_s in V	N_s	step up or step down
240	2000	12		
	3600	9	135	
33 000		11 000	5000	
	50	3	20	

4 A transformer is used to operate a 12 V model train from the 230 V mains supply.

a What is the turns ratio of the transformer?

b Is it a step-up or step-down transformer?

Within the transformer casing there is a rectifier. This converts the a.c. output of the transformer to a d.c. output.

c What would you notice if you tried to run the train on 12 V a.c.?

5

a What are eddy currents?

b Why is it important to reduce eddy currents in a transformer?

On close inspection it is noticed that the core of a transformer is laminated.

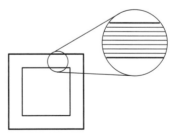

c What does 'laminated' mean in this context?

d Explain how the laminations help to reduce eddy currents.

6 A 9 V radio takes a current of 2 A from the secondary coil of a transformer.

a Calculate the power of the radio.

The supply voltage to the transformer is 240 V and the primary current is 0.08 A.

b Calculate the power input to the transformer.

c Compare your answers to parts **a** and **b**. What do you conclude about the efficiency of the transformer. Explain your answer.

8.6 Generating electricity

Key points

- Electricity is generated on a large scale by rotating electromagnets within coils of wire.
- Conventional power stations burn fossil fuels to: heat water, produce steam, turn the turbines, rotate the electromagnets, generate electricity.
- Our supply of fossil fuels is decreasing rapidly, so alternative energy sources must be found.
- Different generation methods raise different social and environmental issues.

1

a Explain the differences between a permanent magnet and an electromagnet.

b List the advantages and disadvantages of permanent magnets and electromagnets.

c Generators at power stations have large electromagnets that rotate inside stationary coils. Why are electromagnets used rather than permanent magnets?

2 The block diagram below indicates the main processes in a coal-burning power station.

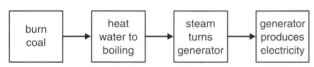

At each stage, state the energy change that takes place.

3 Wind turbines are increasingly being used to generate electricity.

Recently, a large wind turbine has been built on the outskirts of a small market town in Norfolk.

a What do you think are the main disadvantages of supplying some of the town's electricity needs from this turbine?

b What advantages does the wind turbine have over coal, gas or oil-fired power stations?

4 Two possible sites for wind farms (a group of wind turbines is called a wind farm) have been suggested in the North East of England. One is on the coast at the site of a disused chemical works.

Many of the buildings are still there and the land is thought to be toxic. The other site is much higher and is on heather clad moorland.

List the possible advantages and disadvantages of each site and give reasons for your answers.

5 One of the waste products from burning fossil fuels is carbon dioxide gas. This contributes to the 'greenhouse effect'. The diagram below indicates how a garden greenhouse works.

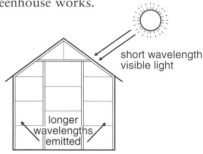

short wavelength visible light

longer wavelengths emitted

a Explain carefully what is meant by the greenhouse effect in the context of power generation.

Surprisingly, perhaps, a majority of the World's population lives near sea ports.

b Why is this relevant to the problem of global warming?

IDEAS AND EVIDENCE

6 It is often said that the heat from power stations and the greenhouse effect could cause a rise in the average temperature around the world. This would melt significant amounts of the polar ice caps, so causing sea levels to rise. Using your knowledge of physics (and geography) explain why melting ice in the Arctic would not have the same effect as melting ice in Antarctica.

8.7 Power transmission

Key points

- A considerable amount of power can be wasted as heat when electricity is transferred over large distances.
- Power is transmitted at high voltages so that less power is lost.
- Transformers are used to step up the voltage at the power station and step it down at its destination.

- Transformers only work with alternating current. This is why mains electricity is a.c.
- H Less power is lost at high voltage because, for a given amount of power, the current, and hence the heat loss ($= I^2R$), are low.

---

1 The diagram below shows how electricity from a power station is distributed around the country.

a Copy the diagram and fill in the missing labels.

b Explain briefly why power is transmitted at high voltages.

c Mains electricity is a.c. Explain briefly why the arrangement shown in the diagram would not work with d.c.

---

2 The high voltages used for transmission of electricity are dangerous. This is one reason for having high pylons to keep the cables well above ground level.

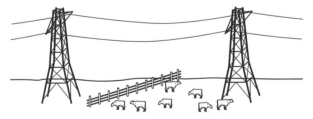

It would be very dangerous to fly a kite near overhead cables even though the kite string is made of an insulating material. Why is it dangerous?

---

3 Two plans have been put forward for transmitting electricity from a power station. The cable resistance is 10 Ω.

Plan 1: step the voltage from the generator up to 20 000 V and transmit at 1000 A.

Plan 2: step the voltage from the generator up to 200 000 V and transmit at 100 A.

a Calculate the power transmitted in Plan 1.

b Calculate the power transmitted in Plan 2.

c Calculate the power lost in Plan 1.

d Calculate the power lost in Plan 2.

e Which plan would you recommend? Explain your answer.

---

4 Overhead power cables are made from a steel core with aluminium wires around it.

The diagram shows the cross-section of a cable.

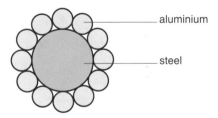

Copper is not used to make the wires, although it is a better conductor than either aluminium or steel.

a Why do you think copper is not used?

b Explain the reasons for the use of aluminium and steel. The following information may be helpful.

- A steel wire has about 40 times the resistance of an aluminium wire of the same dimensions.
- Steel is over 3 times more dense than aluminium.
- The force required to break a steel wire is about 10 times larger than the force require to break an aluminium wire of the same dimensions.

A1.1 Logic gates

Key points

- Simple logic circuits use mechanical switches.
- Logic gates use electronic switches with electrical signals for inputs and outputs. At any time, the voltage level at the output depends on the voltage levels at the inputs.
- The input signal for a logic gate is either a high voltage (about 5 V) or a low voltage (about 0 V).

- The output voltage of a logic gate is high or low depending on its input signals.
- AND, OR and NOT are different logic gates.
- A truth table summarises the way in which the output of a logic circuit varies depending on the state of the inputs. Truth tables use '1' for 'high' and '0' for 'low'.

---

1 Explain what the following are and give a simple example of each:

a a mechanical switch

b a logic gate

c '0' and '1', 'high' and 'low'

d the input voltage to a gate

e the output voltage of a gate

f a truth table.

2 For each of these three logic gates, AND, OR and NOT, draw the circuit symbol, say what the gate does and write out its truth table.

3 The following logic gates use mechanical switches. For each one write out a truth table and say what sort of gate it is.

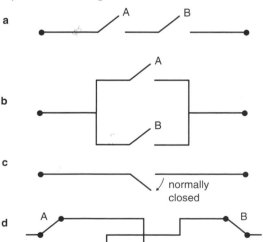

a

b

c normally closed

d

Gates **b** and **d** are similar but differ in one important respect. What is that respect and why is it important?

e Explain how circuit **d** is used to control lights on a staircase and why circuit **b** would not work satisfactorily.

4 The following circuit has four separate switches that can be either 'on' or 'off'. How many possible arrangements of 'on's and 'off's are there? How many of them result in the circuit being 'on'?

Hint: Draw the truth table for the four switches and fill in all the possibilities. It should then be clear which of the possibilities result in the circuit being 'on'.

5 Explain the effect of using a NOT gate after each of the following components and say how the new circuit could be used:

a after a temperature sensor detecting an increase in temperature

b after a light sensor detecting the onset of darkness

c after a moisture sensor detecting the rising level of water in a tank.

6 Explain what gates you would use in the following situations:

a an outside lamp that comes on after dark but has a switch that allows you to switch the light off manually

b a doorbell that can operate from two separate bull pushes

c a computer responding to the return key or the mouse

d a microwave that does not work until the door is closed

e a car body press that is turned on at a main control but will not operate until the guard is in place and then the start button depressed.

A1.2 Inputs and outputs

Key points

- Switches, light dependent resistors (LDRs) and thermistors can be used, together with resistors, to provide input signals for logic gates.
- Relays controlled by logic gates can be used to switch large currents in circuits containing heaters, motors, lights and locks.

H A light emitting diode (LED) and series resistor can be used to indicate the output of a logic gate.

H A relay is needed to switch on a current in a mains circuit using a logic gate; the mains voltage is much too high to be connected directly to the output of the logic gate.

1 Construct a table to show which of the following devices are input devices and which are output devices. At the side of each one, if possible, draw its circuit symbol.

- buzzer
- heater
- indicator lamp
- LDR
- LED
- magnetic lock
- moisture sensor
- motor
- pressure switch
- reed switch
- relay
- switch
- thermistor.

2 Some of the input devices from question **1** are digital sensors because they are either 'on' or 'off'. Explain the difference between analogue and digital input devices and suggest some advantages of each type. Draw a diagram to show the extra circuitry needed to use an analogue sensor and how it is then connected to the input of a gate.

3 The following diagram shows the construction of a simple relay. Copy the diagram and explain how the relay works.

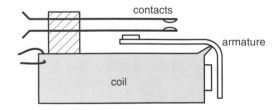

contacts

armature

coil

4 What sensors would you use to detect the following conditions? Explain simply how each one would work:

a water level

b the temperature of an oven

c an open or closed door

d night or day

e the presence of a coin in a slot

f up or down

g rain or sunshine.

5 Some output devices need a relay for their safe operation.

a Explain why a low voltage motor requires a relay even though it will run off the same supply as the gate.

b Explain why a mains lamp requires a relay even though the current may not be large.

6 The diagram below shows a simple moisture detector. Explain how you would use it to detect rainfall.

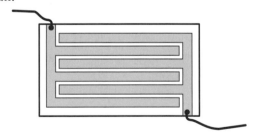

7 Draw a circuit diagram to show how the moisture sensor from question **6** can be used in series with a resistor to provide an input voltage to a NOT gate. The input voltage must be 5 V when it is dry and 0 V when it is wet. Show how a buzzer can be connected to the output of the NOT gate so that it sounds when it is raining on the sensor.

Hint: Make the moisture sensor and resistor into a potential divider (see section **A 1.6**) and connect the midpoint to the input of the gate.

8 It is sometimes useful to know the state of the output of a gate. This is achieved by using an LED. Explain why a resistor would normally be connected in series with the LED. If the output of the gate is 3 V and the maximum safe current for the LED is 7 mA, what value resistor would you use?

A1.3 **Electronic systems**

> ### Key points
>
> - An electronic system is a group of complex switches that allows a job to be done.
> - It consists of input, processor and output device.
>
> - An electronic system usually uses a chip with many gates on it.
> - Microchips are very tiny chips, often mounted on a printed circuit board.
> - Logic gates are used as part of an electronic system.

1 Explain what the following terms mean:

a an electronic system

b an input

c the processor

d an output.

Write down some details of an electronic system with its input, output and processor.

2 A simple fire alarm system has two smoke detectors and a test facility. The diagram below shows a possible circuit for the system.

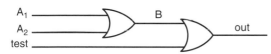

a What sort of logic gate is used?

b Why is this type of gate needed?

c Finish the truth table for the system.

inputs			output	
A1	A2	test	B	C
0	0	0	0	0
0	0	1	1	1

3 A gas boiler heats the water for the central heating. This is controlled by a time switch, S, and a room thermostat, T. It also heats the hot water as it is required. A flow switch, F, detects the flow of water as a tap is turned on.

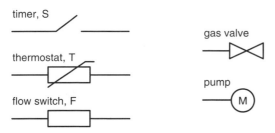

Finish the circuit diagram and draw a truth table for the system.

4 In question **3**, the demand for hot water overrides the central heating. Redraw the circuit for the gas boiler and add one other gate that will control the central heating pump.

Hint: The pump will need to be on when the flow switch is not on, the temperature is low and the timer is on. The inputs to this gate will come from within the circuit you have already drawn.

5 What is a 'chip' and why are they so important in the production of electronic systems?

6 A timer chip is used to turn a flashing warning light on and off. The main key switch has a high output when it is on. As the unit is only required to work in the dark, it is also controlled by a light sensor. This sensor gives a high output in the light. The timer produces pulses that are repeatedly '1' and '0' for half a second at a time.

a Draw a circuit diagram showing the inputs, processor and output.

b Draw a truth table for your system.

Hint: Use one gate to combine the effect of the key switch and the light sensor. Then use a second gate to combine the output of the first gate with the output of the timer.

7 A teenager makes traffic lights for a road junction on her model railway layout. She has a timer that produces on-off pulses at two frequencies, one twice the frequency of the other.

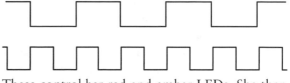

These control her red and amber LEDs. She then uses a logic gate and a NOT gate to control the green LED. Construct a truth table for several sequences of the traffic lights.

A1.4 More truth tables

Key points

H   Logic gates can be combined to produce various outputs.

H   A NAND or NOR gate is formed when the output of an AND or OR gate becomes the input of a NOT gate.

H   Truth tables for a combination of logic gates can be worked out.

H   A circuit of logic gates can be assembled to fit a given truth table.

1   Explain what the following components are. Draw the circuit symbol and give a simple explanation of the possible use of each one:

a   a NOT gate

b   a NAND gate

c   a NOR gate.

Write out a truth table for each gate.

2   NAND and NOR gates are formed when the output of AND and OR gates become the inputs of a NOT gate. Draw the circuit diagrams and complete the truth tables to show that this is the case.

Hint: This is what you would do for the NAND gate.

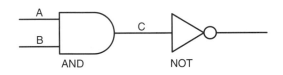

inputs			output
A	B	C	

3   Show, by constructing a truth table, that a NAND gate with both inputs connected together behaves like a NOT gate.

4   A car park entry barrier is raised by either inserting the correct coins 'C' or a card pass 'P'. The barrier contains a counter and will only rise if there are spaces vacant 'S'. Construct a truth table for the barrier.

5   Show, by constructing truth tables, that these pairs of logic circuits have equivalent outputs.

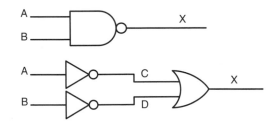

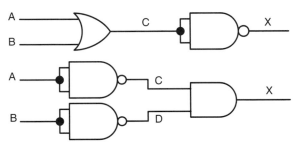

Now draw an equivalent circuit made entirely from NAND gates.

6   In a furniture store, the heat of the sun on the roof was setting off the sprinkler system. The problem was solved by having three detectors connected to a logic circuit which controlled the sprinklers and an alarm. The detectors are an infrared smoke detector, a carbon monoxide sensor and a heat sensor. Each sensor produces a '1' output when activated. A combination of sensors is required to set off the sprinklers. Construct a logic circuit that is consistent with this truth table for the sprinkler and the alarm.

heat sensor	gas sensor	smoke detector	sprinkler	alarm
0	0	0	closed	off
0	0	1	closed	on
0	1	0	closed	on
0	1	1	closed	on
1	0	0	closed	off
1	0	1	open	on
1	1	0	open	on
1	1	1	open	on

A1.5 The bistable and latch

Key points

- Some circuits store information – they have a memory.
- The simplest memory circuit uses two NOR gates that are cross-connected.
- A circuit with two stable states is called a bistable.
- Bistables are used in computers.
- When only one output is used it is known as a latch.

H Two NAND gates can also be used to make a bistable or latch.

H A brief 'high' signal at one input causes a permanent 'high' signal at the output.

H A brief 'high' signal at the other input causes a permanent 'low' signal at the output.

H A low signal at *both* inputs leaves the output unchanged.

1 Explain the following terms:

a a NOR gate   e set and reset

b a bistable circuit   f memory

c a latch   g RAM.

d a flip flop

2 The circuit shows two NOR gates cross connected to make a S-R bistable.

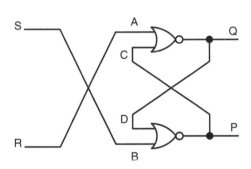

	S	R	A	B	C	D	Q	P
1	0	0	0	0	1	0	0	1
2	1	0	0	1	0	1	1	0
3	0	0	0	0				
4	0	1						
5	0	0						
6	1	1						

a Complete the truth table, line 3, to show that if S returns to '0' accidentally, the bistable remains set, Q = '0'.

b Complete lines 4 and 5 to show what happens when it is reset, P = '1', and then returned to '0' accidentally.

c Line 6 will show the output when both inputs are '1'.

3 The truth table in question **2** shows that the bistable is stable in either output mode when both inputs are zero. Draw a truth table for S, R, Q and P with the four normal input combinations. Include both possible outputs in the first line.

4 A bistable can be constructed using NAND gates in the same positions as the NOR gates, but with S connected to A and R connected to B. Answer questions **2** and **3** for a NAND gate bistable.

Hint: The NAND gate bistable has indeterminate outputs when both inputs are '1's. Start with both inputs '1' and choose an output combination. Work on from there to complete the truth table. This time check that returning both inputs '1' does not change the state of the output. When you come to repeating question **3**, include both possible outputs in the last line.

5 The diagram below shows a S-R bistable used as a latch to debounce a switch.

Clean contact between the contacts of a switch is rare and the latch ensures the switch is set on the first contact. Explain how the latch is useful in a counter operated by a mechanical switch.

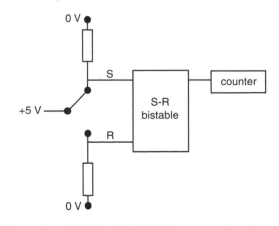

A1.6 **Potential divider**

Key points

- A potential divider uses two resistors to split a voltage into two parts.
- The voltage is divided in the ratio of the two resistances.
- If one resistor is variable the output voltage can be varied.

- Light dependent resistors and thermistors can be used to provide a variable voltage to turn on a light or sound a bell.
- **H** The size of the output voltage can be calculated if the resistance values are known.

---

1 Explain the principle of a potential divider. In the diagram below, E is the emf of a cell and 'x' and 'y' are two resistors which make up a potential divider.

Draw a circuit for each example in the table and calculate the voltage, V in volts, across 'y'.

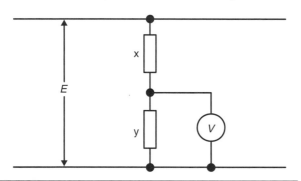

E in volts	x in ohms	y in ohms	V in volts
12	4	2	
6	20	10	
24	60	40	
15	15	20	

2 The diagram below shows an analogue strain gauge. The resistance of the gauge increases with the strain.

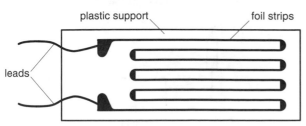

plastic support   foil strips

leads

a Copy the diagram and explain what happens when the strain is increased.

b Suggest how you could use the strain gauge together with a steel bar and an electronic voltmeter to measure weight.

3 You have a large supply of 50 ohm resistors and a 12 V car battery.

a Draw circuit diagrams to explain how you would arrange these resistors to provide the following voltages:

   i 6 V, 3 V and 9 V from the same circuit
   ii 2 V and 8 V from the same circuit
   iii 5 V and 10 V from the same circuit.

b You find, in a box, two 6 V light bulbs, one labelled 300 mA and one labelled 30 mA. Explain why only the 30 mA bulb will light from your 6 V supply.

c Is it possible to connect the bulbs to the battery to check that they are both working? Hint: Simply connecting them in series across the battery will not work. Look at the currents and apply what you know about potential dividers to see why. It may even blow one of the bulbs. Using one of the 50 ohm resistors may help.

4 The diagram below shows a typical arrangement of resistors used for supplying a varying voltage to the input of a logic gate.

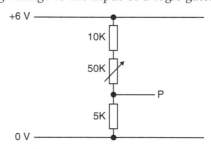

a What is the range of resistances of the variable resistance?

b What is the range of possible voltages at P?

c What is the purpose of the 10K resistor?

5 A radio volume control takes a fraction of the signal from the first stage of the amplifier and feeds it into the next stage. Explain how this works.

A1.7 Thermistors and LDRs

Key points

H   A light dependent resistor (LDR) can be used with a fixed resistor to provide a signal for a logic gate that varies with light intensity.

H   A thermistor can be used with a fixed resistor to provide a signal for a logic gate that is temperature dependent.

H   An LDR or a themistor can be used with a variable resistor to provide a signal with an adjustable threshold for a logic gate.

1 Explain what the following components are. Draw its circuit symbol and give a simple explanation of the possible use of each one.

a an LDR

b a thermistor.

2 The diagrams below show two analogue sensors.

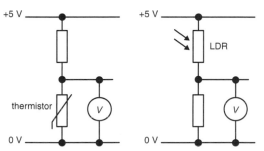

Copy the diagrams and explain what happens to the voltages, V, when the temperature goes up and when it gets lighter.

3 The diagram below shows a circuit designed to maintain the temperature of a fish tank.

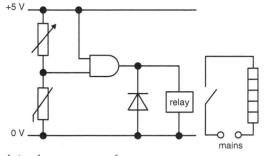

Explain the purpose of:

a the thermistor

b the variable resistor

c the relay

d the diode.

It would seem simple to use a thermistor in series with the heater coil. Why would it be unwise to use a thermistor of this type in this way?

4 An electric hand dryer has a heater and a fan. Both heater and fan are switched on by a infrared proximity switch and the unit is protected from overheating by a n.t.c. thermistor in the airflow. This turns off the heater but not the fan. Draw a possible logic circuit for the hand dryer and explain how it works. Assume, for this question, that the proximity switch contains an LDR so that the IR is reflected onto the LDR when hands come close.

5 The circuit below shows an LDR which is used to control an outside security light which comes on after dark. It has a test switch built into the circuit.

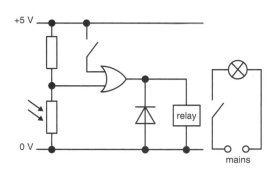

a How could you improve the circuit so that the light level at which the security light came on could be altered.

b What sort of events could make the light come on for short periods in the day, and make the light go off for short periods in the night? How could you improve the circuit to stop this happening?

6 Draw a logic circuit which will turn a fan heater on when the daytime temperature falls. A control panel should have a temperature control and on-off push buttons to set the system manually.

Hint: Use potential dividers to provide the inputs for a logic gate and use a S-R flip flop to override the automatic controls. Don't forget, the fan heater should be controlled by a relay.

A2.1 Refractive index

1 Explain what is meant by:

a angle of incidence   f critical angle

b angle of reflection   g optically dense

c angle of refraction   h more dense

d the normal   i dispersion of light.

e refractive index

2 Clear plastic blocks can be made with refractive indices equal to 1.40 or 1.42. However, a block of plastic refractive index 1.40 has a portion which did not mix properly when it was made and has a refractive index of 1.42. Even though the block is perfectly clear a wavy streak can be seen in the block. Explain why. You may find it helpful to draw a ray diagram.

3 In a sandwich of transparent materials, the direction of a ray of light changes in each new material. Joe says that the direction of the ray is the same whenever the material is the same. Check this out for these two examples. See if the direction of the ray is the same for:

a the two sections of air around a glass/plastic/glass sandwich

b the two sections of plastic in an air/plastic/water/plastic/air sandwich.

a glass		
plastic		
glass		

	air
b plastic	
water	
plastic	
	air

Use the following refractive indices:

glass = 1.50   water = 1.33
plastic = 1.42   air = 1.00

Pick your own angle of incidence. Because you are not dealing with a straightforward case of refraction you will have to use this formula:

$$n_1\sin\theta_1 = n_2\sin\theta_2$$

where medium 1 is the first medium at a boundary and medium 2 is the second.

4 A ray of light enters the air at the top of the Earth's atmosphere. The density of the air increases closer to the Earth. The path of the ray of light will bend. Which way will it bend? Draw a diagram of the Earth and the atmosphere to show what happens.

5 Calculate the speed of light in the materials listed in this table.

substance	refractive index	speed of light in m/s
air	1.00	3×10^8
water	1.33	
plastic	1.42	
glass	1.50	
dense glass	1.92	
diamond	2.42	

Now plot a graph of speed of light against refractive index. Use the graph to find the speed of light in glass of refractive index 1.61 and the refractive index of the glass where the speed of light is 2.5×10^8 m/s.

6 For the same piece of glass, red light has a refractive index of 1.520 and blue light 1.538.

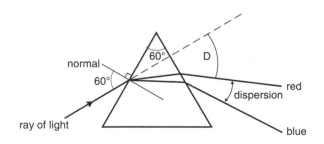

Copy the diagram. Plot the red ray through the prism and calculate the angle of deviation, D. Do the same for the blue ray. Hence calculate the angle between the red and blue rays. This is called the dispersion.

A2.2 How convex lenses work

Key points

- A convex lens is thicker in the centre than at its edges.
- A convex lens converges light and is sometimes called a converging lens.
- Ray diagrams allow us to work out how a convex lens behaves.

1 Explain what is meant by:

a convex

b a convex lens

c a convex lens is the same as a converging lens.

2 Draw a labelled diagram to explain the following terms when they are applied to a converging lens:

a principal axis   c principal focus

b optical centre   d focal length.

3 Finish the following ray diagrams to show the effect of a converging lens. Draw a second set of ray diagrams to show what would happen if you use a stronger lens (a lens of higher power).

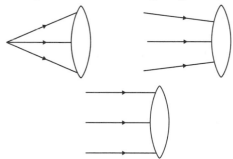

4

a What is a distant object?

Joe says that it is possible to find the focal length of a lens fairly accurately using just the lens, a piece of white card and a ruler.

b Draw a diagram to show how he would arrange the lens, card and ruler.

c What would he use as an object?

d What would he measure?

e How would he check his result?

5 The lights in a swimming pool shine down upon the surface of the water. The light travels through the water and illuminates the bottom of the pool.

a When there are swimmers in the pool they disturb the surface of the water and wavy patches of brighter light appear on the bottom of the pool. Explain, using diagrams, how these patterns are created.

b A ripple tank is used to observe phenomena associated with waves, such as reflection and interference. Bright patches of light are formed on white paper beneath the ripple tank. Explain how these patches are an exact copy of what is happening in the tank shown below.

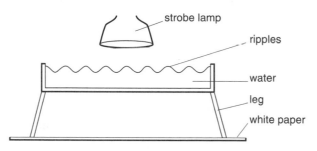

6 Draw a series of ray diagrams to find the position and size of the image in a converging lens. Use squared paper if possible. Make the focal length 2 cm and the height of the object 1 cm.

Label f and 2f on both sides of the lens.

Draw the object at a distance of 5 cm from the lens. Draw, very neatly, the three rays used to construct ray diagrams. Measure the image distance and the height of the image. Repeat this for object distances of 4 cm, 3 cm and 2 cm.

a Construct a table for your observations:
  - position of the object in terms of f and 2f
  - size of the object
  - way up of the object
  - position of the image in terms of f and 2f
  - size of the image
  - way up of the image
  - whether the image is real or virtual.

b What do you notice about the changing position of the ray through the optical centre?

A2.3 Uses of convex lenses

Key points

- How a convex lens is used depends on where the object is placed relative to the focal point.
- A camera has the object at a relatively large distance from the focal point.
- A projector has the object between the focal point and a distance twice the focal length from the lens.
- A magnifying glass has the object between the focal point and the lens.

1 Explain simply what the lens does in the following items:

a a camera

b a projector

c a magnifying glass

d a door spy hole

e a book magnifier

f a telescope.

2 Draw a ray diagram to find the position and size of the image in a converging lens when it is used as a magnifying glass. Use squared paper if possible. Make the focal length 2 cm and the height of the object 1 cm. Label f and 2f on both sides of the lens. Draw the object about halfway between the focus and the lens. Draw another diagram for a object slightly closer to the lens. Consider the position of the ray through the optical centre of the lens and write down the possible positions and sizes of the image. Where is the best position for the object for a large clear image?

3 In a camera, most of the pictures (images) will be taken of distant objects. What is the relationship between the focal length of the lens and the distance between the lens and the back of the camera? Telephoto lenses have longer focal lengths than standard lenses. Explain, simply, why they stick out further from the front of the camera.

4 Draw a diagram showing the essential parts of a camera. Label the lens, the film, the image, the aperture and the shutter. Explain how you would change the camera to:

a focus on a nearer object

b take the same picture in brighter light

c take a picture of a fast moving object

d take a picture with near and distant objects in focus.

e Films have different speeds. Explain what this means and why we need a choice of film speed when we buy a film. Give a few examples.

5 The camera and the eye both produce small images of distant objects. By considering their structure and mode of operation, make a table of their similarities and differences.

Hint: Consider how the incoming light is controlled, how the image is detected, the sensitivity of the detector and how they are both focused.

6 Slide projectors are used to produce a large image of a small coloured film.

a Draw a ray diagram, using the dimensions in question **2**, for a lens that is being used to project a slide onto a screen.

b Explain why for a household slide projector:

  i the slide is put in the projector upside down

  ii the lens is moved when the projector is focused

  iii there is a curved mirror behind the bulb and a condenser lens in front.

7 A sunshine recorder is constructed out of a large glass sphere and a stand carrying a paper chart. The recorder is set up so that the centre of the chart faces due south. The hours of the day are marked across the chart from left to right. When the Sun shines it burns a mark on the card.

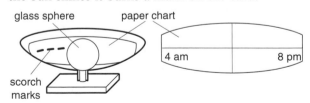

Explain why:

a the chart is scorched when the Sun shines

b the sphere is the best shaped lens for recording the sunshine during the day

c you can tell how bright the sunshine was

d you can measure how long the sunshine lasted during the day

e this data is important to a seaside resort.

A2.4 Resonance

Key points

- Every object vibrates with its own natural frequency.
- The natural frequency of an object depends, among other things, on its mass.

- Resonance occurs when an object is subjected to a vibration at its natural frequency.

1 Explain what the following terms mean and give an example of each:

a natural frequency

b forced vibration

c resonance

d period.

2 Put these situations into a table to show whether the vibrations are 'forced' or 'natural':

a a tuning fork vibrating

b a tuning fork making a table vibrate

c a child swinging freely on a swing

d trees swaying gently in a breeze

e a flag flapping in the wind

f a man swinging a key on a chain

g a church bell ringing.

Include one example of each of your own.

3 A child on a playground swing has a period of 3 seconds and a frequency of 0.33 Hz. What happens when the child is pushed with:

a a frequency of 0.30 Hz?

b a frequency of 0.33 Hz?

c a frequency of 0.26 Hz?

Explain which frequency would be best for a heavier child on the next swing.

4 Explain what happens to the period of oscillation when increases are made to:

a the length of a pendulum

b the mass of a pendulum bob

c the mass on the end of an oscillating spring

d the length of an oscillating spring by adding another spring in line with the first

e the length of a vibrating wire

f the mass of a vibrating wire.

5 A passenger buys a cup of coffee during a train journey and leaves it on the table to cool a little. Almost immediately she observes a pattern of circular ripples on the surface of the coffee. There were four circular waves in a cup approximately 8 cm across.

a What was happening to make the ripples?

b If the speed of surface waves was 15 cm/s, what was the frequency of the vibration that caused them?

IDEAS AND EVIDENCE

6 The first bridge across the Tacoma Narrows in America was well known for resonant oscillations in the wind that funnelled down the gorge. It became a tourist attraction. People would have an afternoon out to watch the oscillating bridge. One day, even though the wind was not strong, the oscillations changed to being torsional and each oscillation became larger than the last. The bridge's designer drove his car onto the centre of the bridge but eventually realised that the oscillations were not going to die down and he staggered off, along a nodal line running down the centre of the road. Eventually, after several hours, the bridge broke up and fell into the river below.

a What are 'resonant oscillations'?

b What are 'torsional oscillations'?

c Why did the oscillations build up in the wind 'even though the wind was not strong'?

d Why could the designer walk down a 'nodal line'?

A2.5 Resonance in strings

Key points

- The natural frequency of a vibrating string depends upon its length, mass and tension.
- A node is a point on a vibrating string having zero displacement.
- An antinode is a point on a vibrating string having maximum displacement.

- The frequency of a vibrating string depends on the number of nodes.
- A string can have different modes of vibration depending on the number of nodes.
- The quality of a note depends on the modes of vibration.

1　The strings on a piano vary in thickness and in length. Long, heavy strings produce the low notes and short, light strings produce the high notes. Explain the following:

a why long strings make lower notes than short strings

b why heavy strings make lower notes than light strings.

Hint: When answering questions of this sort, where two things are compared, you must say why short strings produce high notes as well as saying why long strings produce low notes; i.e. you must deal with both parts of the question.

2　Joe says there are three ways of changing the note produced by a guitar. Plucking different strings is one of them.

a What are the other two?

b Whilst trying to explain what he meant to a friend, he touched one of the strings in the middle and plucked it gently near the end. The string made a much higher note than usual. 'That was a fourth way of changing the note,' he said, 'one I had forgotten.' What was happening here?

3　Explain what the following terms mean and give one example of each to illustrate your answer:

a a stationary wave
b the frequency
c a mode of vibration
d a node
e an antinode
f the quality of a note.

4

a The frequency of a vibrating string depends on the number of nodes. Explain what this means.

b A metal wire is stretched between two supports 1 m apart. The fundamental note has a frequency of 120 Hz. Draw diagrams to show the first five harmonics. Label each one with the wavelength and the frequency. The first harmonic is done for you.

c Use the wave equation to calculate the speed of sound in the wire.

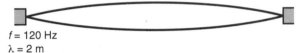

$f = 120$ Hz
$\lambda = 2$ m

5　The diagram below shows three different modes of vibration of a wire stretched between two supports.

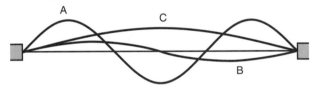

Copy the diagram and answer these questions.

a Which mode has the highest frequency?

b Which mode has the longest wavelength?

c Which mode has the smallest amplitude?

6

a Copy the diagram below, adding arrows that show the direction of movement of the string.

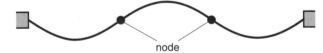

node

b Use the words 'in phase' and 'out of phase' to complete the following sentences.

　i All parts of a stationary wave, between two adjacent nodes, vibrate _____.

　ii The parts of a stationary wave either side of a node vibrate _____.

7　The sound of a violin is quite different from the sound of a guitar. This is because the quality of the notes is different. Draw diagrams of the waveforms produced by the two instruments to help you explain the difference.

A2.6 Resonance in pipes

Key points

- The natural frequency of a vibrating air column depends on its length.

- Modes of vibration depend on whether the pipe in which the air is vibrating is a closed pipe or an open pipe.

1 You have a crate of empty milk bottles. Explain:

a what happens when you blow across the top of an empty milk bottle and a clear note is produced

b how you could use this effect to play a tune.

2 The family of instruments that produce sound when you blow them are called wind instruments. Some, like the clarinet, have a reed which starts the vibration. Brass instruments, like the trumpet, rely on the player's lips to form the reed. Put these instruments into a table to show whether they are 'brass' or 'reed' instruments:

- bassoon
- bugle
- clarinet
- french horn
- oboe
- saxophone
- trombone
- trumpet
- tuba.

3 A bugle is a long tapered tube which produces natural harmonics. The player changes the note by blowing harder or softer and allowing their lips to vibrate at the different frequencies. Explain how it is possible to play simple tunes.

4 A brightly coloured flexible plastic tube open at both ends and 75 cm long was purchased at the seaside. When it is held at one end and swung round it produces a clear note. Swinging it round faster produces several higher notes. Sam managed to obtain five harmonics. Explain how those harmonics were formed. If the speed of sound was 330 m/s, what were the frequencies of those harmonics?

5 A bugle player uses harmonics to play tunes. Draw wave diagrams of the harmonics in an open tube to explain how the notes are produced. Generally the fundamental is a difficult note to obtain and it is much lower than the other notes the bugle produces (why?). It is therefore not often used in bugle 'calls'. The next five harmonics are used. If the speed of sound in air is 330 m/s and the bugle is a tube 1.30 m long, calculate the frequencies of the notes that are produced.

6 Draw sine wave 'A' as carefully as you can. Make the amplitude 2 cm and the wavelength 8 cm. Draw one wavelength. On the same axes, draw sine wave 'B' which has twice the frequency and half the wavelength. Draw two wavelengths.

Hint: sin 0° = 0, sin 45° = 0.71 and sin 90° = 1, so for amplitude 2 cm these values will be 0 cm, 1.42 cm and 2 cm. You need four sections like this for one wavelength.

Now add the instantaneous values together and, on the same axes, plot a third wave which is the sum of the other two. You may have to chose in-between values to add together to obtain a smooth curve.

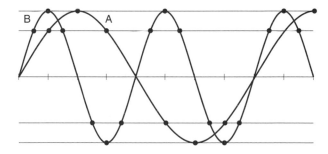

If these waves were being produced by a pipe, you would hear the sound of a flute. You may like to try adding other harmonics. Use your drawings to explain what the 'quality' of a note means.

7

a What is the difference between noise and a musical note?

b What does 'resonance' in sound mean?

c A resonance tube filled with water is adjusted so that it resonates to sound of a frequency of 600 Hz produced by a small loudspeaker. Water is then let out so the tube is three times longer than it was. The tube still resonates to a frequency of 600 Hz. Why is this? How could you use this tube to measure the speed of sound?

A2.7 Interference

Key points

- Interference is caused when two waves meet.
- Constructive interference has a reinforcing effect.
- Destructive interference has a cancelling effect.

1

a Explain what 'in phase' and 'out of phase' mean when referred to waves.

b If waves are 'coherent', what features do they have in common?

c Explain, simply, what the principle of superposition says. What does it say about coherent waves that arrive at a point 'in phase' and waves that arrive at a point 'out of phase'.

---

2 Explain how two coherent waves are produced for experiments with:

a sound

b light

c microwaves

d water (as in a ripple tank).

3

a Draw a diagram of a ripple tank and explain how you would use it to demonstrate constructive and destructive interference with water waves.

b Draw the pattern that you would see and explain how it was formed.

---

4 Nick offered to provide the sound system for a disco and placed his two large speakers at the front of the room. When he had connected them to the amplifier there was a problem with the sound down the centre of the room. The sound round the edges was fine but it was quieter than usual in the centre. Joe suggested that Nick had connected the speakers so that they were out of phase with each other and reversing the connections to one speaker would solve the problem.

a What was happening in the centre of the room?

b What happened in the centre of the room when the connection was reversed?

c Why does this action not just move the quiet area to another part of the room?

Draw diagrams to illustrate your answers.

---

5 All electromagnetic waves exhibit interference. The diagram below shows an experiment with microwaves.

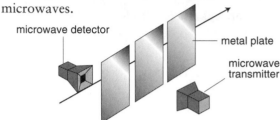

The microwave detector is connected to a sensitive meter and gives an output in proportion to the intensity of the microwaves falling on it.

a Describe what you would observe as you move the detector along the line.

b Explain why microwaves are detected behind the centre plate even though it blocks out the transmitter completely.

c Draw a wavefront diagram to show what is happening behind the central plate.

d The wavelength of microwaves used in this experiment is about 3 cm. How wide should the gaps between the metal plates be?

---

6 The most convenient way to demonstrate interference with light in the laboratory is with a laser and a double slit.

a Why is light from a laser more suitable than light from an ordinary light bulb?

b What do you see on the screen?

c How could you show that light was coming through both slits? What would you expect to happen?

d What would happen to the fringes if the screen was moved back twice as far?

e If the experiment was performed with blue light which has a shorter wavelength then the red laser light, how would you expect the fringes to change?

f This experiment is used to find the wavelength of light. Explain why it is therefore an important experiment in science.

A2.8 The nature of light

Key points

- Some properties of light can be explained by considering light to behave as a wave.
- Some properties of light can be explained by considering light to behave as a particle.
- This phenomenon is known as wave particle duality.

1 Define what is meant by the following features of a wave:

a the frequency

b the wavelength

c the displacement of a point on the wave

d the amplitude of the displacement

e the period

f the intensity of the wave

g the speed of the wave.

2 Define what is meant by the following features of a particle:

a its mass

b its speed

c its momentum

d its energy.

3 Write down two examples of each of the following types of waves. Include a typical wavelength and speed:

a sound waves

b water waves

c waves from earthquakes

d light waves

e radio waves.

4 For interference to take place the size of the gap must be similar to the wavelength of the radiation. The de Broglie relationship relates the wave and particle properties to the Planck constant:

wavelength × momentum = the Planck constant

and so gives a way of finding the wavelength associated with things we normally think of as particles.

a Find the wavelength of an electron.

$m_e = 9.11 \times 10^{-31}$ kg

$v = 1.00 \times 10^6$ m/s

the Plank constant = 6.63×10^{-34} J s

b What size gap would cause electron interference? Where might you find such small gaps?

c What would be your wavelength if your mass was 50 kg and your speed 2 m/s as you walked through a doorway? Would the gap be small enough for interference to take place? Are you normally a particle or a wave?

5 Sort the following pairs of statements into whether they refer to waves or to particles. Make a table with the headings 'waves' and 'particles' and write each statement in the correct column:

a i energy comes in lumps – 'quanta'
ii energy comes in a continuous range of values

b i energy is proportional to the frequency
ii energy is proportional the amplitude squared

c i easily shows interference
ii easily shows momentum

d i how energy travels through space
ii how energy interacts with surfaces.

6 In the photoelectric effect, the photons in UV light have enough energy to release electrons from the surface of a piece of zinc. If the zinc rests on top of a negatively charged electroscope, this loss of electrons is enough to discharge the electroscope.

One UV photon has about the right energy to release one electron. IR light does not release electrons. One IR photon does not have enough energy to release an electron nor will the electrons 'store' energy from several photons as you might expect on a wave theory.

a Draw an electroscope with a piece of zinc resting on top illuminated by UV light. Show electrons being released.

b Why will IR light not release electrons?

c What evidence is there from this experiment that UV light is behaving like a particles and not like a wave?

A3.1 Linear motion

Key points

- A negative acceleration is a deceleration.
- **H** Acceleration can be found from the gradient of a velocity–time graph.
- **H** Displacement can be found from the area under a velocity–time graph.
- **H** There are some useful equations that describe motion with constant acceleration.

1 The table below shows the results of an experiment to find the acceleration produced by an athlete using a cycling machine.

time in s	velocity in m/s
0	0
10	2.5
20	5.0
30	7.5
40	10.0
50	10.0
60	10.0
70	10.0
80	8.0
90	6.0
100	4.0

a Plot the graph of velocity against time.

b Using your graph, comment on the acceleration:

  i during the first 40 s

  ii from 40 s to 70 s

  iii from 70 s to 100 s.

2 The velocity–time graph below shows the motion of a lorry travelling along a straight road.

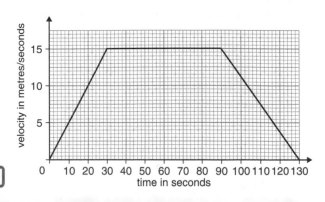

a Using the graph, find the acceleration of the lorry over the first 30 s.

b Using the graph, find the acceleration of the lorry over the final 40 s.

c How does your answer to part **b** show that the lorry is decelerating?

d From the graph, find the total displacement of the lorry in m.

3

a Write down the three equations that describe motion with constant acceleration.

A train pulls out of a station and accelerates steadily for 20 s, until its speed reaches 7.5 m/s.

b Calculate the train's acceleration.

c Calculate the distance that the train travels in the 20 s.

The train then travels at a constant speed of 7.5 m/s for 5 minutes.

d How far does it travel in that time?

The train then takes a further 30 s to decelerate steadily to a halt.

e Calculate the train's deceleration.

f Calculate the distance that the train travels in the final 30 s.

g Calculate the total distance travelled for the whole journey.

h What is the average speed of the train for the whole journey?

4 A builder was working in a church. A floorboard collapsed and the builder dropped a hammer into the hole. He noticed that some time elapsed before he heard the hammer hit the ground below! Experiments found that the time taken was 1.1 s.

a Find the depth of the hole.

b Find the speed at which the hammer hit the ground.

A3.2 Projectile motion

Key points

- An object thrown horizontally in the Earth's gravitational field describes a parabolic path.

H In the absence of friction a projectile has a constant horizontal velocity.

H The vertical velocity of the projectile increases steadily due to the effect of gravity.

---

1 The diagram below shows a transport plane carrying aid to earthquake victims.

bundle

plane is here when the bundle hits the ground

The plane drops a bundle of blankets. The plane then continues to fly at constant horizontal velocity.

a Copy the diagram.

b Assuming that there is no air resistance (and no parachute) show on the diagram where the bundle will hit the ground.

c Explain your answer in terms of the horizontal and vertical velocities of the bundle.

2 A stone is dropped from the top of a cliff. It takes 6 s for the stone to hit the ground below.

a How high is the cliff?

b Calculate the speed of the stone as it hits the ground.

c If the same stone were dropped from a cliff of the same height on the Moon, how long would it take to reach the bottom of the cliff? (Acceleration of free fall on the Moon is 1.6 m/s².)

3 The diagram below shows an experiment set up in a school laboratory.

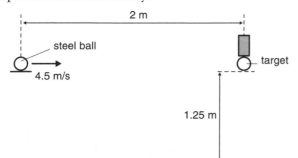

A steel ball is aimed directly at the target. An electronically operated mechanism releases the target at exactly the moment that the steel ball is fired. Use the information on the diagram to answer the following questions.

a How long does it take for the target to fall to the ground?

b Describe the path that the steel ball will take.

c Does the steel ball hit the target?

d Explain your answer in terms of the horizontal and vertical velocities of the steel ball and the target.

4

a Draw a diagram to show the motion of a ball thrown into the air at an angle to the vertical of 45°.

'In the absence of friction a projectile has a constant velocity.'

b Explain the above statement in terms of the force(s) acting on a projectile.

---

5 A stone is dropped down a well. It hits the water surface after 2 s. Copy the table.

time in s	speed in m/s	distance fallen in m
0	0	0
1	10	
2		

Calculate the speeds and distances and complete the table.

A3.3 Momentum

Key points

H   Momentum = mass × velocity. It is measured in kg m/s (or N s).
H   Momentum is a vector quantity.
H   Force = rate of change of momentum.
H   Impulse = force × time = change in momentum.

H   The total momentum before a collision always equals the total momentum after a collision, as long as no external force acts.
H   Momentum conservation can be applied to many practical situations.

1 A model rocket, mass 0.15 kg, was launched from a launch pad fixed in the ground. The rocket took off vertically at a velocity of 5 m/s.

a   What was the momentum of the rocket before launch?

b   Calculate the momentum of the rocket after take-off.

c   How do you account for the difference between your answers in parts **a** and **b**?

2 A model cannon shoots out a cork that has a mass of 0.5 g. The velocity of the cork is 3 m/s.

a   What is the momentum of the cork before it leaves the cannon?

b   Calculate the momentum of the cork immediately after it leaves the cannon.

c   State the Principle of Conservation of Momentum.

d   What does the Principle of Conservation of Momentum tell you about the movement of the model cannon as the cork shoots out?

3 A garage attendant was surprised to be asked to give a lorry a push as the battery was flat. He was even more surprised when he leant on the back of the lorry and the slight movement of the lorry was enough to start the engine.

Explain, in terms of momentum, how the garage attendant was able to get the lorry started.

4 The following diagrams show model trucks on straight model railway tracks. Copy each diagram and use the Principle of Conservation of Momentum to calculate the missing values. Show your working in each case and include the correct units.

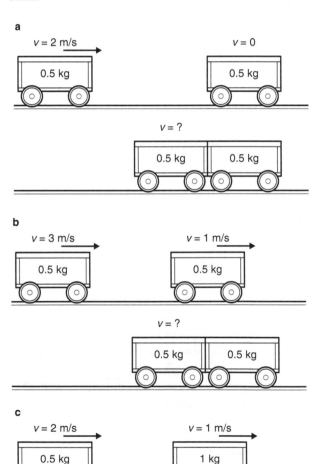

A3.4 Rockets and jets

> ### Key points
>
> - Rockets carry their own supply of fuel and oxygen. This enables them to move out of the Earth's atmosphere.
> - Jet engines are similar to rockets but do not leave the Earth's atmosphere.
>
> H The exhaust gases forced out from the back of the rocket give a force on the rocket propelling it forwards.
>
> H The momentum of the exhaust gases backwards is equal to the momentum of the rocket forwards.

1 The diagram below shows a rocket on a launch pad.

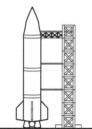

a What would happen if the thrust were less than the weight of the rocket?

b What would happen if the thrust were equal to the weight of the rocket?

c What would happen if the thrust were greater than the weight of the rocket?

2 A balloon has been inflated but the end has not been tied. The balloon is held still.

a What is the momentum of the balloon?

The balloon is now released.

b Explain in terms of the forces on the balloon and the air and in terms of momentum how the balloon will move.

c Explain how this is an application of Newton's Third Law of Motion.

3 The velocity–time graph below shows the motion of a Bonfire Night rocket from launch until it runs out of fuel.

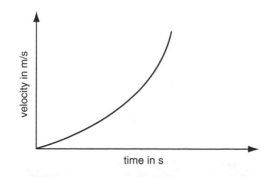

a How can you tell from the graph that the acceleration of the rocket is increasing?

b What happens to the mass of the rocket during the time shown by the graph line? Explain your answer.

c Explain why the acceleration increases during the time shown by the graph line.

d Copy and complete the graph to show the motion of the rocket from launch until it hits the ground.

4 The diagram below shows the basic parts of a rocket.

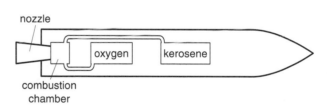

Explain briefly how a rocket works (include the word 'momentum').

5 A rocket uses 1800 kg of fuel and oxygen every second. The exhaust gases are ejected from the rocket at a speed of 900 m/s. The exhaust gases are the products of the reaction between the fuel and the oxygen that the rocket carries.

a What mass of exhaust gases is ejected every second?

b Calculate the change in momentum of the exhaust gases every second.

c What is the change in momentum of the rocket every second?

d What is the thrust on the rocket? Explain your answer in terms of Newton's Second Law of Motion.

A3.5 Car crashes

Key points

- When vehicles collide the occupants can be injured due to the rapid deceleration.
- If the deceleration is spread over a longer time the forces acting on the occupants are reduced.

- Cars are designed so that they stop more slowly in the event of a crash. Crumple zones, air bags and seat belts all help to keep the occupants safe.

1 Explain, in terms of Newton's First Law of Motion, why the passengers in a car may be thrown forward in the event of a crash if they are not wearing seat belts.

2 A car, mass 850 kg, is travelling at 30 m/s. A lorry in front stops suddenly but the car driver manages to avoid a collision and comes to a halt 10 s after applying the brakes.

a Calculate the deceleration of the car.

b Calculate the distance travelled by the car in the 10 s.

c Calculate the average braking force.

3 The diagram below shows the crumple zones in a car.

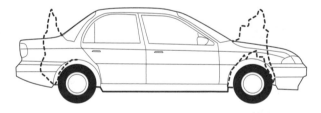

a Explain how the crumple zone spreads the deceleration of the car over a longer time in the event of a crash.

b Explain how the longer deceleration time decreases the forces acting on the occupants of the car. Your explanation should include reference to Newton's Second Law of Motion.

4 Car seat belts are designed to stretch by a small amount in the event of a crash.

a Explain why, in terms of the forces acting on a car passenger, it is important that the seat belt can stretch.

b Why would it be dangerous if the seat belt stretched too much?

5 In the event of a car crash, the air bag will inflate quickly to prevent the driver from hitting the steering wheel.

a Explain, in terms of the behaviour of gas molecules, how the air bag inflates.

b Explain, also in terms of the behaviour of gas molecules, how the air bag prevents injury to the driver.

6 A car was involved in an accident. It was travelling at 10 m/s when it hit a stationary vehicle and stopped in 0.1 s. The driver had a mass of 70 kg and the passenger's mass was 80 kg.

a Calculate the deceleration of the car.

The driver was wearing a seat belt so his deceleration was the same as that of the car.

b Calculate the force acting on the driver to slow him down.

The passenger was not wearing a seat belt so he continued to move at 10 m/s until he hit the windscreen. He then decelerated over 0.04 s.

c Calculate the deceleration of the passenger.

d Calculate the force acting on the passenger to slow him down.

The driver had either not seen the stationary vehicle or did not react quickly enough.

e Suggest as many reasons as you can for the accident.

A3.6 Measuring heat

Key points

- Specific heat capacity is the energy required to raise the temperature of unit mass of a substance by one degree.
- When an object is heated the energy transferred is equal to mass × specific heat capacity × temperature change.

- In many processes energy is ultimately dissipated as heat.
- This thermal energy is spread so thinly throughout the surroundings that it cannot be transferred into other useful forms of energy.

---

1   The specific heat capacity of pastry is significantly lower than the specific heat capacity of strawberry jam.

a   What is meant by the term 'specific heat capacity'?

b   How might the difference in specific heat capacities of pastry and strawberry jam be noticeable in practice?

---

2   The diagram below shows the apparatus used to find the specific heat capacity of water.

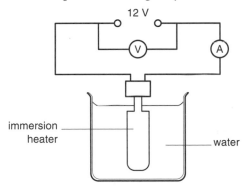

The readings taken during the experiment are as shown below:

mass of water, m = 0.200 kg
voltage, V = 12 V
current, I = 2.0 A
heating time, t = 750 s
initial temperature, θ_1 = 20 °C
final temperature, θ_2 = 40 °C

a   Calculate the power of the heater.

b   Calculate the energy transferred from the heater to the water.

c   Calculate the specific heat capacity of water.

The accepted value for the specific heat capacity of water is 4200 J/kg °C.

d   Explain why your calculated value is higher than 4200 J/kg °C.

e   Suggest ways of making the experiment more accurate.

---

3   A student heated some water in a beaker.

a   Explain what happens to the water in terms of the behaviour of the water molecules.

b   The temperature increased from 20 °C to 80 °C and the mass of the water was 250 g. Calculate the energy transferred to the water. The specific heat capacity of water is 4200 J/kg °C.

c   The amount of energy supplied by the Bunsen burner is greater than the amount calculated in part **b**. What happens to the energy that is not used to heat the water?

---

4   A sample of metal was heated in boiling water for a few minutes and then transferred quickly to the cold water. The temperature rise of the water was recorded. The experiment was repeated with samples of different metals.

The results are shown in the table below.

metal	temperature rise in °C
aluminium	14
iron	11
lead	3
copper	9

The aim of the experiment was to be able to arrange the metals in increasing order of specific heat capacity.

a   List the variables that you would keep constant when carrying out this experiment.

b   Assuming that the readings are accurate and are the result of experiments in which the variables were properly controlled, list the metals in order of increasing specific heat capacity.

c   Suggest some precautions you would take to ensure an accurate experiment.

A3.7 **Efficiency**

1 For each of the energy transfer devices listed below state the useful type(s) of energy output and the wasted type(s) of energy output:

a a steam engine

b a loudspeaker

c a washing machine

d a light bulb

e a radio

f an electric drill

g a car

h a gas cooker.

2 If you wanted to communicate with a friend who lives at the other end of the road, you could shout!

a Shouting is not a very efficient way to communicate, however. Explain what happens to the sound energy and why your friend will probably not hear you.

It would be more efficient to speak to each other on the telephone.

b Explain, in terms of energy changes, how your message is transferred by telephone.

c Explain, in terms of energy waste, why the telephone conversation is more efficient than shouting.

3 In an experiment a student heated some water in a beaker from room temperature (20 °C) to boiling point (100 °C). The mass of water used was 0.200 kg. The heating time was 5 minutes.

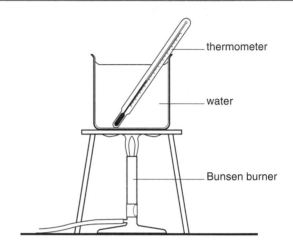

a Calculate the energy required to heat the water. The specific heat capacity of water is 4200 J/kg °C. The energy output of the Bunsen burner was 190 000 J/minute.

b Calculate the energy output of the Bunsen burner in 5 minutes.

c Calculate the energy efficiency of the heating. Show your working.

d Suggest reasons for the efficiency being less than 100%.

e Suggest a simple way to improve the efficiency.

4 An electric winch has a power of 200 W. It is used to lift a mass of 10 kg at a speed of 0.5 m/s.

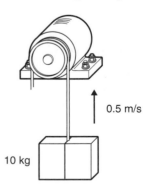

a Calculate the weight of the mass.

b Calculate the useful work done by the winch.

c Calculate the efficiency of the winch.

d Suggest why the winch is less than 100% efficient.

Glossary (TB 1–8)

Terms in **bold italic** type are higher tier material.

A

acceleration (2.4) rate of increase of velocity

acid rain (8.6) rain containing sulphurous acid (e.g. caused by coal-burning power stations), which damages stonework and wildlife

activity (5.3) number of disintegrations, per second or per minute, in a radioactive source

aerial (4.3) a device for receiving or transmitting radio signals

air resistance (2.5) retarding force on an object moving through the air

alpha particle (5.1) a helium nucleus (2 protons and 2 neutrons); it is emitted when some radioactive nuclei decay

alternating current (a.c.) (7.4) frequent change of direction of an electric current or voltage

alternator (8.4) generator of alternating current

ammeter (1.2) instrument used to measure electric current

ampere (A) (1.2) unit of electric current

amplitude (3.2) the maximum displacement of a wave from its rest position

antineutrino (5.1) a small particle emitted when a neutron changes into a proton and an electron

apparent depth (3.6) the depth a dense transparent object appears to be – effect caused by refraction

asteroid (6.1) one of many small rocks orbiting the Sun between Mars and Jupiter

asthenosphere (4.8) a layer of flowing mantle on which continental plates move

atomic number (5.1) the number of protons in the nucleus of an atom

B

background radiation (5.1) radioactivity that is always present around us

bacteria (5.5) simple organisms, some of which cause disease

balanced (2.6) state of equilibrium

becquerel (Bq) (5.3) unit of radioactivity equal to one decay every second

beta particle (5.1) a high-speed electron emitted when some radioactive nuclei decay

Big Bang (6.3) the explosion by which scientists believe the Universe began expanding

Big Crunch (6.3) one possible future for the Universe – the reverse of the Big Bang

black dwarf (6.2) a faded white dwarf (*see* **white dwarf**)

black hole (6.2) part of space with such a large pull of gravity that not even light can escape

blue supergiant (6.2) large star with short life

braking distance (2.9) distance moved by a car in stopping after the brakes are applied

C

cancer (5.4) tumours which grow out of control, eventually killing normal tissue

carbon brushes (8.2) conduct current to and from the coil in electric motors and generators

catapult (effect) (8.1) resultant force on an electrical conductor in a magnetic field that makes the conductor move

centripetal force (6.1) force on an object moving in a circle which acts towards the centre of the circle

charge (7.1) property of some sub-atomic particles; product of electric current and time ($Q = It$)

circuit breaker (7.5) automatic switch which 'trips' (turns off) if the current exceeds a specified value; can be reset by turning the switch on

coal-burning power station (8.6) power station where electricity is generated by burning coal to produce steam.

combined heat and power (CHP) (2.12) heat normally wasted from power stations is used to heat nearby houses and factories

comet (6.1) a collection of dust and small ice lumps, which orbit the Sun in a very elongated elliptical orbit

compression (3.1) part of a longitudinal wave where the particles are closer together than normal

concave (3.3) curving inwards

conduction (thermal) (2.11) the way in which thermal energy is transferred in solids

conductor (electric) (7.1) a material that allows an electric current to pass

conservation of energy (8.3) principle that energy cannot be created or destroyed

constructive boundary (4.8) boundary between separating plates where lithosphere is being formed

continental drift (4.7) the theory which accounts for the movement of the continents over a long time

convection (2.11) the way in which thermal energy is transferred in fluids (liquids and gases)

convection current (2.11) movement of a fluid due to convection

conventional current (7.3) direction of current from positive to negative around a circuit

converge (3.3) to come towards a point

convex (3.3) curving outwards

core (4.7) the central part of the Earth

coulomb (C) (7.3) unit of electric charge; charge due to a current of 1 A passing for 1 s

couple (2.1) two equal forces acting in opposite directions a distance apart

critical angle (4.4) the angle of incidence which produces an angle of refraction of 90° as light passes into a less dense medium

crumple zone (2.7) front or rear of a car designed to buckle and bend in an accident

crust (4.7) the outer layer of the Earth

cumulative (5.6) increasing by repeated addition

D

daughter nuclide (5.3) an isotope produced as a result of radioactive decay

decay (5.3) the splitting of a radioactive nucleus with the emission of ionising radiation

deceleration (2.4) slowing down; negative acceleration

degraded (energy) (2.12) energy that is so spread out it cannot be transferred into other useful forms

destructive boundary (4.8) boundaries between colliding plates where lithosphere is being destroyed

diffraction (3.7) the spreading out of a wave as it passes through an opening of a similar size (or smaller than) its wavelength

diffuse (3.4) spreading out in many directions or scattering

digital signal (4.4) signal which is either off or on so any small variations are not taken into account

diode (1.1) electrical component that conducts current in one direction only

direct current (d.c.) (7.4) current or voltage due to charge flow in one direction

displacement (2.3) straight line distance between two points

dissipate (1.1) change into non-useful form, waste (energy)

diverge (3.3) to go away from a point

DNA (5.6) deoxyribonucleic acid – a molecule which carries coded genetic information

Doppler effect (6.3) waves from moving objects appear to have shorter or longer wavelengths

double insulation (7.5) describes an electrical appliance having no electrical connections to the case so no earth connection is needed

drag (2.5) frictional force opposing the motion of an object through a fluid

dynamo (8.4) current generator

E

earth (wire) (7.4) part of household wiring that only carries a current if there is a fault, melting the fuse

earthquake (4.6) this occurs where rocks break suddenly at a fault

echo (3.4) the reflection of sound

echolocation (4.5) using echoes to measure distance and hence find invisible objects

eddy current (8.5) current induced (e.g. in a transformer core) causing energy loss

electric current (1.1, 7.3) rate of flow of electric charge

electric shock (7.5) symptoms that follow the passage of an electric current through the body

electromagnetic wave (3.1) wave propagated as a periodic disturbance of the electromagnetic field

electrostatic precipitator (7.2) electrostatic device fitted to the chimneys of power stations and factories to reduce pollution

electron (1.1, 7.1) negatively charged particle

endoscope (4.4) used to look inside the body, consisting of a lighted optical fibre and a viewing device

energy (1.1, 2.8, 7.4) the ability to do work

energy efficiency (2.12) ratio of the useful energy output to the total energy input of a machine

epicentre (4.6) a point on the Earth's surface immediately above the focus of an earthquake

equilibrium (2.1) state that exists when a system is not changing (e.g. when forces are balanced)

exciter (8.6) d.c. generator providing current for the rotating electromagnets in a power station

F

Faraday's Law (8.3) the induced voltage is proportional to the rate of cutting magnetic field lines

fault (4.6) point of fracture of rock strata due to forces acting

filament (lamp) (1.3) very thin wire (in a lamp) heated to a high temperature by an electric power source so that it emits light

film badge (5.2) worn by people who work with ionising radiation to measure their exposure to radiation

Fleming's left-hand rule (8.1) rule for the direction of the force on a current-carrying conductor in a magnetic field

Fleming's right-hand rule (8.3) rule for the direction of the induced current when a conductor moves in a magnetic field

fluorescent (4.1) the emission of light by certain substances when struck by light or electrons

focus (4.6) the origin of an earthquake

focus (of mirror and lens) (3.3) the point to which rays of light converge or from which they diverge

follow through (2.7) practice of keeping the racquet, club etc. in contact with the ball for as long as possible to give it maximum velocity

force (2.1, 7.1) a push or pull exerted by one object on another

fossil fuel (8.6) fuel produced by the slow decay of dead things

frequency (3.2, 7.4) the number of complete waves passing a point in one second

friction (2.5, 7.1) contact force opposing the motion of one object sliding past another

friction compensated (2.7) the raising of one end of a runway so

that the gravitational force down the slope is exactly equal to the friction force up the slope

fuel (8.6) substance burned to provide a source of energy

fuse (7.4) thin piece of wire which melts if the current through it is too high

G

gamma ray (4.3, 5.1) most energetic and penetrating electromagnetic radiation emitted in nuclear decay

gas-fired (power station) (8.6) power station in which the fuel used is gas

Geiger-Müller tube (5.2) a detector of radioactivity

generator (8.4) device that uses mechanical energy to produce electricity

geo-stationary orbit (6.1) a satellite in orbit above the equator taking 24 hours for each orbit

glancing angle (3.4) the angle between a ray of light and the incident surface

global warming (8.6) the heating of the Earth due to man-made causes such as the greenhouse effect

gradient (2.2) measure of steepness; often related to graphs, it is the tangent of the angle between a line and the x-axis

gravitational field strength (2.5) force acting on unit mass due to gravity; on Earth it is 10 N/kg

gravitational potential energy (2.8) energy due to the Earth's gravitational pull on an object and its position above the ground (= mgh)

gravity (2.4, 6.1) attractive force between masses (e.g. an object and Earth)

greenhouse effect (8.6) trapping of the Sun's rays beneath gas layers in the atmosphere, causing global warming

H

half-life (5.3) the time taken for half the nuclei in a sample of radioactive material to decay

hertz (Hz) (3.2) the unit of frequency (one oscillation per second)

hydroelectric (power) (8.6) use of the kinetic energy of falling water to produce electricity

I

image (3.6) a reproduction of an object formed by a lens or mirror

incident ray (3.4) ray of light

travelling towards a reflecting or refracting surface

induced current (8.3) current produced when a conductor cuts a magnetic field

induced voltage (8.3) voltage produced when a conductor cuts a magnetic field

induction (7.1) appearance of a voltage across a conductor when it moves with respect to a magnetic field

inert (7.2) non reactive

infrared (4.1) part of the electromagnetic spectrum with wavelength just longer than visible light

insulated (thermally) (2.12) surrounded by a material that does not readily transfer thermal energy

insulator (electrical) (7.1) material that does not allow an electric current to pass through it

insulator (thermal) (2.11) material that does not readily transfer thermal energy

ion (7.3) an atom that has gained or lost electrons

ionisation (5.2) the addition or removal of electrons from an atom

ionosphere (4.3) a layer of the upper atmosphere able to reflect long- and medium-wave radio waves

iron core (8.2) on which a coil of wire is wound to increase the magnetic field

isotope (5.1, 6.2) an atom of an element having a different mass number but the same atomic number

joule (J) (2.8) unit of energy; $1J = 1N\,m$ or $1kg\,m/s$

kilowatt (kW) (7.4) one thousand watts

kilowatt-hour (kWh) (7.6) commercial unit of electricity (= kW × hours)

kinetic energy (2.8) energy possessed by a moving object (= $\frac{1}{2}mv^2$)

L (Love) waves (4.6) waves which travel through the surface of the Earth

laminated (8.5) thin sheets of iron used to make the core of a transformer, reducing eddy currents

lava (4.7) molten material which is extruded onto the Earth's surface

Lenz's Law (8.3) the direction of an induced current always opposes the change that produced it

leverage (2.1) increasing the turning effect of a force by increasing its distance from the pivot

lift (2.5) upward force on the wing of an aeroplane

light dependent resistor (LDR) (1.1) a resistor whose resistance decreases when the light level increases

light emitting diode (LED) (1.1) a diode that emits light when it is conducting a current

lightning (7.2) discharge between a charged thundercloud and Earth

lithosphere (4.7) the outer part of the mantle and lower part of the crust of the Earth

live (wire) (7.4) a high-voltage wire, with brown insulation, that carries electric current to mains appliances

longitudinal wave (3.1) a wave whose vibrations are parallel to its direction of travel

loudspeaker (8.1) a device which changes electricity to sound

lymphocyte (5.6) a type of white blood cell

machine (2.12) a device that enables a task to be done more easily

magma (4.7) molten rock

magnetic field (8.1) region around a magnet in which there is a magnetic force

mantle (4.7) the layer of the Earth below the crust

mass number (5.1) the total number of protons and neutrons in the nucleus of an atom

metamorphism (4.8) the action of heat and pressure on rocks, which then changes their original state

microwave (4.3) part of the electromagnetic spectrum – wavelength at the short end of radio waves

milliamp (mA) (1.3) one thousandth of an ampere

moment (2.1) turning effect of a force (see also torque)

motor (8.2) a device which uses electricity to produce motion

mutation (5.6) alterations in genetic material which change the cell or virus

mutual induction (8.4) voltage induced in a coil of wire by a changing magnetic field in an adjacent coil

National Grid (8.7) nationwide supply network carrying electricity from power stations to consumers

nebulae (6.2) clouds of gas and dust in space

neutral (wire) (7.4) wire, with blue insulation, kept at 0 V, which provides the return path for mains electric current

neutron (7.1) uncharged particle present in the nucleus of an atom

neutron star (6.2) a small, dense collapsed star

newton (N) (2.8) unit of force; a force of 1 N gives a 1 kg mass an acceleration of $1\,m/s^2$

newton metre (Nm) (2.1) unit used for the moment of a force (force × distance) Nm

no-parallax (3.6) the lining up of object and image

normal (3.4) a line at right angles to a surface

nuclear (power) (8.6) the use of nuclear energy (from fission) to produce electricity

nuclear fusion (6.2) the joining together of light nuclei with the release of energy

nucleus (7.1) the central part of an atom containing protons and neutrons

nuclide (5.1) another name for isotope

ohm (Ω) (1.2) unit of electrical resistance; ohm = volt/ampere

ohmic (1.3) an electrical conductor that obeys Ohm's Law

Ohm's Law (1.3) at constant temperature, the voltage across a conductor is proportional to the current in it

oil-fired (power station) (8.6) power station in which the fuel used is oil

optical fibres (4.4) very thin glass fibres that light passes along by total internal reflection

order of magnitude (3.7) an indication of the size of a number according to its power of ten

P

P (primary) waves (4.6) longitudinal waves from an earthquake

parallel (circuit) (1.2) components connected across the same two points

parent nuclide (5.3) an isotope which undergoes radioactive decay

pay-back period (2.11) time taken to recoup the cost of installing thermal insulation from the savings made on fuel bills

photocopier (7.2) device that uses electrostatics to print a copy of a document

pivot (2.1) point at which a lever is balanced

plane (3.3) a flat surface

planet (6.1) a body which orbits the Sun or any other star, seen only by reflected light

plate (4.8) one of the sections into which the Earth's crust is divided

polar orbit (6.1) a satellite in orbit over the North and South poles of the Earth

pollution (8.6) damage to the environment from man-made causes

power (2.8, 7.4) rate of transfer of energy

power (rating) (7.4) power output of a device when working normally

power loss (8.7) difference between the input and output power of a device

primary (8.5) the input coil of a transformer

prism (4.4) a regular-shaped block of glass or other dense transparent material

proton (7.1) positively charged particle present in the nucleus of an atom

protostar (6.2) a new star formed from collapsing gas and dust

pulse (3.3) a single short burst of sound or other wave

Q

quasar (6.3) very bright distant object giving out large amounts of energy

R

radar (4.3) the use of reflected radio waves to measure distance or locate objects

radial (magnetic) field (8.2) magnetic field in the space between the curved poles of a magnet and an iron core that is aligned with the centre of the core

radiation (5.2) energy which travels as rays, waves, or particles

radiation (thermal) (2.11) part of the electromagnetic spectrum adjacent to red light (infrared)

radiation burns (5.6) caused by exposure to radioactivity, similar to heat burns but take longer to heal

radiation sickness (5.6) sickness caused by exposure to radioactivity

radio (4.1) a band of the electromagnetic spectrum, which is mainly used for communication

radiocarbon dating (5.5) using the activity of carbon-14 atoms in a sample to determine its age

radioisotope (5.1) an isotope which decays by emitting ionising radiation

rarefaction (3.1) part of a longitudinal wave where the particles are further apart than normal

reaction (force) (2.5) force on an object resting on a surface that is perpendicular to that surface

reaction time (2.9) time taken by the brain to respond to a signal (also called thinking time)

real depth (3.6) the actual depth of a dense transparent object

real image (3.6) an image that can be projected onto a screen

red giant (6.2) an average-sized star that expands at the end of its life

red shift (6.3) when a galaxy is moving away from us, the light appears redder than usual

red supergiant (6.2) a large blue supergiant which expands at the end of its life

reflected ray (3.4) ray of light which is travelling away from a mirror

refraction (3.5) the change in direction of light as it passes from one transparent material to another of different density

renewable source (8.6) source of electricity that does not get used up (e.g. wind) or is quickly replaced (e.g. biomass)

repel (7.1) two objects that move away from each other, such as like poles of a magnet

residual current device (RCD) (7.5) detects a very small change in the current in the live and neutral wires of an appliance and breaks the circuit immediately

resistance (1.1) opposition of a circuit component to the flow of charge; ratio of voltage across a component to the current in it

resultant (force) (2.6) single force which equals the sum of two or more other forces

retardation (2.4) see deceleration

reverberation (3.4) the repeated reflection of sound

ring main (7.4) a parallel circuit used to connect 13 A power points in a house

ripple tank (3.3) a shallow tank of water used to illustrate wave phenomena

S

S (secondary) waves (4.6) transverse waves from an earthquake

satellite (4.3, 6.1) an object in orbit around a larger object

scalar (2.3) quantity having magnitude (size) but no direction

sea-floor spreading (4.8) the moving apart of two plates where new crust is created by magma from the mantle

seat belt (2.7) restraint on car occupant to reduce injury in case of accident

secondary (8.5) the output coil of a transformer

seismic waves (4.6) the collective name for L waves, P waves and S waves

seismometer (4.6) an instrument used to measure Earth tremors

semiconductor (1.3) material able to conduct charge to some extent – less than a metal but more than an insulator

series (circuit) (1.2) components connected end to end in a circuit

short circuit (7.5) the by-passing of part of a circuit by a stray wire, reducing the resistance and increasing the current

slip rings (8.4) rings that (with carbon brushes) conduct current to and from the coil in an a.c. generator

Solar System (6.1) the Sun and everything circling around it

sonar (4.5) the use of sound waves and their echoes to measure distance or locate objects

spark counter (5.2) device which sparks when air is ionised, so is used to detect alpha radiation

spectrum (4.1) the distribution of energy emitted from sources arranged in order of wavelength

speed (2.2, 3.2) rate of change of distance (distance/time)

split-ring commutator (8.2) split ring that keeps the forces on the coil of an electric motor in the same direction producing continuous rotation

step-down (transformer) (8.5) transformer that reduces voltage

step-up (transformer) (8.5) transformer that increases voltage

sterilise (5.5) make free from bacteria or other micro-organisms

stopping distance (2.9) distance a vehicle travels from the time the driver sees an obstruction to coming to rest (= braking distance + thinking distance)

streamlined (2.6) shaped to offer the least possible resistance to motion

stroboscope (3.3) instrument used to observe moving objects by making them appear stationary

substation (8.7) where transformers are used to successively step-down voltages from the National Grid for local use

subduction zones (4.8) areas where the oceanic plate descends beneath the continental plate

superheated steam (8.6) high temperature steam produced by boiling water at high pressure in a power station

supernova (6.2) an explosion of a large star at the end of its life

supernova remnants (6.2) glowing cloud of gas thrown out from a supernova

tangent (2.2) straight line that just touches a curve

tectonic (4.8) relating to, causing, or resulting from structural deformation of the Earth's crust

tension (2.5) a force in a stretched object

terminal velocity (2.10) the velocity of a falling body when the air resistance, acting upwards, is equal in magnitude to the weight, acting downwards

thermistor (1,1, 4.2) an electronic component whose resistance changes with temperature

thermograph (4.2) a picture formed by recording differing temperatures

thinking distance (2.9) how far a car travels before the brakes are applied, while the driver is still reacting

thinking time (2.9) see reaction time

thrust (2.5) force spread over an area; push or pull due to a rocket engine

toner (7.2) powdered ink used to produce a print in a photocopier

torque (2.1) the turning effect, or moment, of a force, especially a couple

total internal reflection (4.4) reflection inside a material when the angle of incidence exceeds the critical angle

tracer (5.4) a radioisotope introduced into a system so that its path can be followed

transformer (8.5) device used to increase or decrease alternating voltages

transmission (8.7) movement from one place to another (e.g. electricity via the National Grid)

transverse wave (3.1) a wave whose vibrations are at right angles to its direction of travel

trench (4.8) formed when one of the Earth's plates moves up and over another

turns ratio (8.5) ratio of the number of turns on the primary coil of a transformer to the number on the secondary coil

ultrasound (4.5) sound of high frequency – above 20 000 Hz – which is inaudible to humans

ultraviolet (2.6, 4.1) part of the electromagnetic spectrum with wavelength just shorter than visible light

unbalanced (2.6) system not in equilibrium, having a resultant force or moment

V

Van de Graaff generator (7.1) machine which produces a very high voltage by electrostatic means

variable resistor (1.1) resistor whose resistance can be changed

vector (2.3) quantity having magnitude (size) and direction

velocity (2.3, 3.2) the rate of change of distance with time in a straight line (displacement/time)

vibration (3.1) the to and fro motion of a particle or of an elastic solid about an equilibrium position

virtual image (3.6) an image which cannot be projected onto a screen – no light passes through it

visible light (4.1) the region of the electromagnetic spectrum to which our eyes are sensitive

volcanic ash (4.7) molten rock blasted out from volcanoes

volt (**V**) (1.2) unit of voltage ($1\,V = 1\,J/C$)

voltage (1.2) energy converted in an electrical component when unit charge passes through it (= energy/charge)

voltmeter (1.2) instrument used to measure voltage

W

watt (**W**) (2.8, 7.4) unit of power equal to 1 joule/second

wavefront (3.3) the instantaneous position of a wave at right angles to its direction of motion

wavelength (3.2) the distance between two successive points of identical displacement on a wave

weight (2.1) force on an object due to gravitational attraction (= mg)

white dwarf (6.2) a small star which has collapsed when its fuel has run out

work (2.8) work is done when a force moves in the direction of the force; work done = energy transferred = force × distance moved in the direction of the force

XYZ

X-rays (4.1) high energy, penetrating electromagnetic waves of short wavelength

Glossary (TB A1–A3)

Terms in *bold italic* type are higher tier material.

A

air bag (A3.5) installed in cars; designed to inflate if the car decelerates rapidly, protecting the occupants

amplitude modulation (A2.7) changing a radio wave's amplitude by the addition of a signal wave

AND (gate) (A1.1) a circuit with two inputs that gives a 'high' output only when both inputs are 'high'

antinode (A2.5) a point on a stationary wave with maximum amplitude

B

beats (A2.7) phenomenon which occurs when two notes of close but different frequencies are sounded together

binary code (A1.5) a digital counting system using only two digits, 0 and 1

bistable (A1.5) a switching circuit with two stable states

bit (A1.5) short for binary digit

C

carrier (A2.7) a radio wave onto which is added a signal wave

chip (A1.3) a small piece of semiconducting material (usually silicon) which contains millions of circuit elements, and forms an integrated circuit (IC)

closed pipe (A2.6) a tube, in which air is vibrating, closed off at one end

collisions (A3.5) impacts between two or more objects

condenser (A2.3) a system of lenses which collects light to focus it

conservation (of momentum) (A3.3) if no external force acts, the total momentum of a system before a collision equals the total momentum afterwards

constructive interference (A2.7) a reinforcement of waves to produce a larger amplitude

crumple zones (A3.5) areas at the front and rear of a car that are designed to buckle in a crash so that the car takes longer to stop and the force on the occupants is reduced

D

destructive interference (A2.7) a cancellation of waves to produce a smaller amplitude

digital (A1.5) able to take only a certain number of values, such as 0 and 1 in logic circuits

diminished (A2.2) as applied to an image which is smaller than the object

dispersion (A2.1) the spreading out of a ray of light into a wider beam as it is refracted to produce a spectrum

dissipated (A3.6) scattered or spread out

E

efficiency (A3.7) ratio of the useful energy output to the total energy input in an energy transfer process

erect (A2.3) as applied to an image which is the same way up as the object

F

flip-flop (A1.5) another name for a bistable switching circuit

focal length (A2.2) the distance between the optical centre and the focal point

focal point (A2.2) the point through which rays parallel and near to the principal axis pass after refraction at a convex lens

forced vibration (A2.4) an externally applied vibration which causes another object to vibrate

fuel (A3.4) source of energy

fundamental (A2.5) the main natural frequency of vibration of a string or air column

G

gate (A1.1) an electric circuit that can be either 'on' or 'off' in response to certain input signals

H

harmonic (A2.5) a multiple of the fundamental frequency which occurs when a string or air column vibrates

heat engine (A3.7) machine that depends on a rise in temperature in order to work

I

impulse (A3.3) the product of a force and the time for which it acts

input (A1.3) anything that goes into an electronic circuit

insulation (thermal) (A3.6) use of a material that is a bad conductor of heat to reduce energy loss or gain from an object

inverted (A2.2) as applied to an image which is upside down compared to the object

inverter (A1.1) a device that reverses an input signal (see NOT gate)

J

jet turbine (A3.4) an engine in which the exhaust gases from burnt fuel leave in one direction propelling the object attached to the jet turbine in the opposite direction

L

latch (A1.5) a bistable circuit with only one output that remains switched on even when the original signal is switched off

logic (gate) (A1.1) decision making circuit that uses electronic switches (see gate)

M

magnified (A2.3) as applied to an image which is larger than the object

moisture sensor (A1.2) a device that detects the presence of water, producing a related electric signal

momentum (A3.3) the product of the mass and velocity of an object

N

NAND (gate) (A1.4) equivalent to an AND gate with a NOT gate; the output is 'high' as long as both inputs are *not* 'high'

natural frequency (A2.4) the frequency with which any object can be made to vibrate with maximum amplitude

node (A2.5) a point on a stationary wave with zero amplitude

NOR (gate) (A1.4) equivalent to an OR gate with a NOT gate; the output is 'high' when neither input is 'high'

NOT (gate) (A1.1) a circuit with one input that is the reverse of the output; when the input is 'high' the output is 'low' and vice versa

O

open pipe (A2.6) a tube in which air is vibrating open at both ends

optical centre (A2.2) the centre of a convex lens through which we consider light to be undeviated as it passes

OR (gate) (A1.1) a circuit with two inputs that gives a 'high' output when either of its inputs is 'high'

output (A1.3) anything that comes out of an electronic circuit

oxygen (A3.4) an element essential for combustion

P

parabola (A3.2) a curved path as followed by an object thrown horizontally on Earth

path difference (A2.7) the difference in the distance travelled by two waves

phase (A2.7) the amount by which the points of identical displacement of two waves differ

potential divider (A1.6) two resistors, or a single resistor which can be tapped at any point along its length, connected so that part of the voltage across the whole can be obtained

principal axis (A2.2) the line joining the focal points of a convex lens passing through the optical centre

processor (A1.3) something that changes the input of an electronic circuit in a specific way

projectile (A3.2) an object thrown upwards at an angle or projected

horizontally near the Earth's surface

proportional (A2.1) when a straight line graph passes through the origin, the two variables are said to be proportional in that the *y*-variable is a constant multiple of the *x*-variable

Q

quality (A2.5) what a note from a particular instrument sounds like as a result of different harmonics

R

ramp (A3.7) sloping surface that aids movement from one level to another

Random Access Memory (RAM) (A1.5) computer memory containing millions of bistables

range (A3.2) the horizontal displacement of a projectile

real (A2.2) as applied to an image which can be projected onto a screen

recoils (A3.3) moves backwards, as, for example, a gun does when fired

reed relay (A1.2) two easily magnetised strips of nickel-iron, or reeds, activated by a current in a surrounding coil, which make and break a circuit very rapidly

refractive index (A2.1) the ratio of the speed of light in a vacuum to the speed of light in the material

relay (A1.2) an electromagnetic switch that uses a small current to turn on a larger one

reset (A1.5) an input signal to a bistable circuit that restores it to its original state

resonance (A2.4) the vibration of an object at its natural frequency

rocket (A3.4) a jet engine which carries its own oxygen supply so it can travel into space

S

seat belts (A3.5) restraints worn by the occupants of a car to reduce injury in a crash

sensitivity control (A1.7) a variable resistor used in a potential divider to adjust the external condition that changes the input to a logic gate

sensor (A1.1) a device that reacts to an input energy, such as light, and produces a related electrical signal

specific heat capacity (A3.6) energy required to raise the temperature of unit mass of a substance by one degree

stationary wave (A2.5) a wave which exhibits nodes and antinodes formed by the reflection and superposition of one wave upon itself

superposition (A2.7) the addition of two waves to produce a wave whose instantaneous displacement is the arithmetic sum of each individual displacement

system (A1.3) a group of electronic components, consisting of input, processor and output, working together to do something useful

T

truth table (A1.1) a table summarising the way in which the output of a system of logic gates varies depending on the state of the inputs

turbine (A3.7) a device, powered by water or steam, that produces rotation

WXYZ

water wheel (A3.7) wheel turned by the kinetic energy of water

Key data

■ Energy

Kinetic energy, $KE = \frac{1}{2}mv^2$
Potential energy, $PE = mgh$

■ Light

Refractive index, $n = \dfrac{\text{speed of light in a vacuum}}{\text{speed of light in the medium}}$

■ Electricity

Circuit formula: $V = I \times R$

◇ Electrical energy

Electrical power, $P = V \times I$
Electrical energy, $E = P \times t$
1 unit = 1 kWh
Cost of electricity =
    cost per unit × number of kWh

◇ Charge

$V = \dfrac{W}{Q}$ (voltage = work done per unit charge)

Charge and current:
    $Q = I \times t$ (charge = current × time)
Force between charges, $F = \dfrac{kQ_1Q_2}{r^2}$

◇ Atomic energy and quantum theory

Electron volt, $eV = 1.6 \,(\,10^{-19}$ J
Einstein equation: $E = mc^2$
(speed of light, $c = 3 \times 10^8$ m/s)
$E = hf$ (the Plank constant, $h = 6.63 \times 10^{-34}$ J s)
    $\lambda \times p = h$ (p = momentum = $m \times v$)

◇ Space science and orbits

Kepler's third law: T^2 is proportional to r^3
    (T = period of orbit, r = radius of orbit)

◇ Rays and waves

Wave equation: $v = f \times \lambda$
    (velocity = frequency × wavelength)
Refractive index, $n = \dfrac{\sin i}{\sin r}$

$n = \dfrac{1}{\sin C}$

$n = \dfrac{\lambda \text{ in air}}{\lambda \text{ in medium}}$

$n = \dfrac{\text{real depth}}{\text{apparent depth}}$

For adjacent media 1 and 2:
    $n_1 \sin \theta_1 = n_2 \sin \theta_2$ (n = refractive index, θ = angle to normal)

Double slit experiment: $\lambda = \dfrac{a\,x}{D}$
    (a = slit separation, x = fringe width, D = distance from slits to fringes)

Index

X

Z